In Stillness Conquer Fear

Overcoming Anxiety, Panic and Fear

PAULINE McKINNON

johngarrattpublishing

Published in Australia by
John Garratt Publishing
32 Glenvale Crescent
Mulgrave Vic 3170

www.johngarratt.com.au

First published by Newleaf, Dublin, 1999.
First published in Australia by Collins Dove, Melbourne, 1983.

This completely revised edition published by John Garratt, Melbourne, 2008.

Designed and typeset by Lynne Muir
Edited by Cathy Oliver

National Library of Australia Cataloguing-in-Publication entry:
Author: McKinnon, Pauline.

Title: In stillness conquer fear : overcoming anxiety, panic and
             fear / Pauline McKinnon.

Edition: Revised ed.

ISBN: 9781920721787 (pbk.)

Subjects: Agoraphobia. Fear. Anxiety. Meditation —Therapeutic use.

Dewey Number: 616.85255

CONTENTS

Disclaimer

The information provided in this book is intended for general information and guidance only and should not be used as a substitute for
consulting a qualified health practitioner. Neither the author nor the
publisher can accept any responsibility for your health or any side-
effects of treatments described in this book.

To my husband, my friend
To my family, my life.

The Soul sits waiting
she is poised, waiting.
Ever patient, she waits for man or woman
to know her truth;
the truth that frees him or her
from all pain wrought by fear.
The Soul never fears.
Strength is her trademark,
peace is her presence,
wisdom the arrow that flies from her bow.
The Soul is love.
Deep as the core of a precious fruit
she nestles within us.
Yet wide as thunder and wind
her wings of change embrace the world.
All powerful,
all mild,
she is our own –
our whole and special self.

P McK

FOREWORD – 1983 EDITION

Pauline McKinnon has done it. It is those who have done it, rather than those who theorise about it, that we should listen to. By great courage and persistence, trying one approach and then another, she has overcome a distressing fear. She writes with great naturalness, letting us share her frustrations, despair and inward humiliation. Then comes the joy of relief, and the full participation in the life of her family which her phobia had made difficult.

But this book has a wider significance than simply an account of someone who escaped from eight years of fear. It indirectly expresses her own values — what is worthwhile, what life is all about — with a charming openness ringing through and through with sincerity. The book gives hope to those whose lives are crippled by anxiety and agoraphobia; an equally important aspect of the book is that it gives relatives and friends some idea of the suffering of those afflicted in this way, and what they might do to help.

In the text, Pauline makes several references to me. For this I thank her. As with the rest of the book, these are part of the spontaneous expression of what has been in her mind.

I have not read a better account of the symptoms of agoraphobia than this story, beautiful in its simplicity, and penetrating in its clinical accuracy.

Dr Ainslie Meares
BAgS, MD, BS, DPM
July 1982

FOREWORD — 1994 EDITION

In business, it is the successful people who are studied. Who sold the most fridges? Who achieved the best results? And how did they do it? What did they do differently, what did they learn, what did they develop that produced their success?

It seems curious, then, that in recent times medicine often has appeared to study what on one level would appear to be the 'losers'. In a hospital setting, the person who is studied is usually the one with the most obscure illness, the one who takes the longest to diagnose, the one who takes the longest to recover.

In medicine, the successful ones, the ones who recover quickly, are usually off and out of the hospital or waiting room before anyone even notices. Surely these are the very people we should chase down the road and demand answers from. What did you do? How was it that you recovered? What can we learn from you that will help others? Pauline Mc Kinnon is one of those successful patients who did it. She recovered. She even knows how and why she recovered. More importantly, Pauline has the ability to articulately share her experience and knowledge with others — in a way that can help them directly and effectively.

Reading *In Stillness Conquer Fear* could change your life; free you to live fully — in ease, comfort and joy. It is a pleasure to be able to recommend something that I know works so well.

Dr Ian Gawler
OAM, BVSc
Founder and Therapeutic Director
The Gawler Foundation Australia
December 1993

PREFACE

I once read a quotation that has stayed with me always. It went something like this:

> If you want to help me, please don't teach me
> what you have learned from others.
> Teach me something you have learned yourself.

In these pages I hope to teach you what I have learned about fear and anxiety, how these become disorders, how people's lives are affected, how to manage symptoms and how to find relief through therapeutic meditation.

Contrary to when this book was first published, these days anxiety disorders are commonly recognised. For this I believe I have earned some credit as, to the best of my knowledge, *In Stillness Conquer Fear* was the first book published (at least in this country) where the matters of anxiety, panic and fear are discussed at a personal level and where a clear-cut and natural means of help is substantiated.

Over the years I have received a great deal of mail from near and far always with a message of relief, gratitude and hope at having related to the account of another's journey into the anxiety condition. Most have felt alone or embarrassed by the stigma that surrounded fear, yet now we know that anxiety, expressed in many ways, is experienced by millions of others throughout the world. So today, awareness has dramatically increased: professional diagnoses are made, people are given 'stress' leave, a variety of treatments are available, the internet stores countless references, and active support groups for anxiety sufferers can be readily accessed.

Despite all this, anxiety continues to flourish within our society and so I present a new edition of this book to mark 25 years since its first publication, 25 years in professional practice and 30-something years' freedom from the clutches of anxiety and, in fact, agoraphobia.

Because my story reflects the stories of others, some may find it difficult to read. As happens with anxiety, it often seems preferable to avoid or run from what we believe may incite more fear. Such can be our human vulnerability – and inevitably, such can be our loss. So I would like to gently encourage those who feel apprehensive to read on, trusting that the story, its outcome and its message will lead you to the ease you hope for.

My most earnest reason for relating my story is to reach, reassure and assist those whose lives are impaired by fear. And my greatest motivation in this is to continue to raise the profile of meditation as a therapeutic modality for effective and lasting recovery from anxiety conditions. To that I add, though, that for ultimate success, I believe the form of meditation used must follow the precepts set out in this book.

I hope too, that this book will bring understanding to the partners, spouses, families and friends who support the anxious person out of love and loyalty, often without realising just how desperately needed they can be.

I want to speak also to those who do not understand another's human fear and will make statements such as 'stop feeling sorry for yourself' or 'pull yourself together', advice that is useless and insensitive to need. The sufferer has no wish to be distressed by fear, and if it were so straightforward that pulling *anything* together were the solution, he or she would willingly do so!

As anxiety and its accompanying symptoms are manifested in the form of physical or mental distress of some kind, the obvious course of action is to seek medical help. Consequently, I ask for the attention of the many medical doctors who hear the plea of the person in fear, yet may not really answer it. Some do not have adequate information or understanding; many are too busy, while others can respond with indifference or impatience. Unfortunately the inclination in these circumstances is to prescribe anti-depressants or tranquillisers and perhaps offer little hope or an alternative solution. To all health professionals I would like to say: there may be a better and more enriching way to solve some of those anxiety problems you find before you.

It is also important that the public be kept aware of the influence of anxiety within the community. At great cost to society, much productivity can be lost – by employers and employees alike; so awareness and action that can assist should be of prime consideration. Similarly and just as importantly, general public awareness can inspire people to recognise and minimise anxiety and tension in their own lives and thus contribute to a more relaxed and healthy society.

Incidentally, as the World Health organisation predicts that depression, which of course is closely related to anxiety, is likely to be the number one "killer" by the year 2030, society is clearly in great need of anxiety management. It seems the price we are paying for modern progress is the prevalence of high anxiety.

Finally, there is a group of anxiety sufferers I need to single out. Though this book is primarily addressed to adult readers, there are also countless children and adolescents whose lives are spoiled by anxiety. If parents, teachers, counsellors, doctors and other interested adults want to help our young, I believe in these pages you may discover some useful clues. As you would recognise, anxiety does not differentiate between age groups and many young people are suffering greatly, too.

When this book was first published I wrote as a lay-person. While of course my story has not changed, my personal understanding has long been developed by extensive experience as a meditation teacher and psychotherapist, and so my story has expanded.

I now offer it again to all anxiety sufferers so that they may find relief swiftly. I offer it in gratitude to all those people I have known or am yet to know who have or will in some way contribute to my life journey. I especially offer it as a thanksgiving for my own recovery and for the fulfilling life I have been able to lead. Telling my story has always given meaning to my own unpleasant encounter and I continue to do so with the conviction that there is a reason for everything. It is a great joy to know that out of pain, we can find peace and almost accidentally be of help to others – especially if that help can contribute to a greater connection between people – a drop of unification in the ocean of humanity.

To those who have already gained from reading earlier editions, my wish is that anything fresh you find here will take you further up the stairway to success. To new readers, firstly, I wish you personal peace. And then I wish you the contentment that comes with the letting go of fear and the discovery of yourself. I would be pleased to hear your story and learn of your progress.

Pauline McKinnon

INTRODUCTION: OPENING UP ANXIETY

What we do not understand, we do not possess.

Goethe

He was a bachelor of 86, who could well have passed for 68: a colourful, interesting character with many a tale to tell from his long and varied years of living. We shared a carriage on an old country train, and the three-hour journey through endless pastures, green and flood-strewn, flew by very quickly in animated conversation. As the train clattered to a halt at our destination, he looked at me earnestly and said very seriously: 'It's been great to have someone to talk to. Usually the others in the carriage hide behind their magazines and pretend you're not there. People are scared, you know! It's a pity ... but people are scared.'

A few years earlier in my life, that conversation could not have taken place, for I too, would have been scared — not of conversing with a stranger on a train, but of *being* on a train. For eight years my life was impaired by anxiety which led to agoraphobia, the paralysing fear of leaving the safety of home.

During that time and in my desire to conquer that haunting fear, I read a great many books dealing with anxiety, stress and tension. Feeling alone in fear, I longed for something written by someone who had known what I was experiencing, someone with whom I could identify and who really understood my predicament. I never found such a person or such a book – and so in due course, I filled that gap myself.

Gradually, others have ventured into the area with welcome books on anxiety and panic disorders bringing their own personal or professional views into being. Depression too, one of many anxiety symptoms with obvious risks surrounding it, has taken on new supportive meaning, particularly as public figures or glamorous identities confess to their emotions. So today, health professionals diagnose conditions that include *generalised anxiety disorder, panic disorder, social anxiety disorder, obsessive-compulsive disorder, post-traumatic stress disorder, depressive disorders, post natal depression, de-realisation disorder, separation anxiety, phobic disorders and agoraphobia,* which is considered to be the most severe reaction of all.

I prefer to view all of these conditions simply as the progression of escalating anxiety – *and the individual's way of coping with its symptoms.* In their effects, most of these categories overlap each other and most sufferers of any one diagnosis will be familiar to some extent with the effects surrounding any other diagnosis. Unfortunately, anxiety does not simply slot into a category, just because an expert has told it to! So if you have been diagnosed with any one of those 'disorders' you will certainly recognise yourself within this story and be helped by what you read here. And having experienced sufficient escalating anxiety to lead to agoraphobia, I can well appreciate the misery of those people enduring any other anxiety reaction.

Current statistics relating to anxiety state that 10% of our community suffers a severe anxiety disorder and 5% of our community suffers a moderate anxiety disorder. (Source: ADAVIC – the Anxiety Disorders Association of Victoria). And within human nature and quite apart from that range of disorders, millions of undiagnosed people also experience all kinds of mini-fears. How often do we hear the casual comment from young or old: 'I hate crowds,' 'Busy roads frighten me,' 'Oh, no, not a thunderstorm,' 'Don't expect me to make a speech!' The gentleman on the train was certainly right; we are all scared and our fears – even if they are only minor – can take much of the pleasure from life.

Why are people so scared? Why do so many of us, living in civilised and peaceful surroundings, harbour personal fears and insecurities even though we are not necessarily facing obvious danger? Or has the modern world simply arrived at a state of constant anxiety as distressing as the threat of impending disaster?

As I see it, fear, the opposing force to love, is potent within human nature. Either force can underpin our personal judgments, decisions, ambitions, hopes and dreams. Love and its actions brings positive happy outcomes while regrettably, powerful fear can potentially become the dominant reason for our actions and a strong contributing factor in the shaping of each personality. Fear may pretend to lead to success as people meet and master challenges and realise ambitions, but fear can also result in a drive for excessive power. Fear at best can protect us from harm. At its worst it can lead to hatred, anger, control and even warfare – but most importantly, fear creates limitation, and prevents ordinary people from happily fulfilling their lives. And this is how fear gets the upper hand, manifesting as anxiety and producing personal feelings of inadequacy, timidity, shyness, helplessness, lack of confidence, apprehension and loss of a strong sense of self. Within these anxious feelings lie a warning of danger and the need for self preservation at a level of consciousness that we cannot readily access. We can therefore live with anxiety for some time before it increases to the extent of arousing physical or mental symptoms of distress. *It is those symptoms, persisting and intensifying, that lead to a diagnosis of anxiety disorder.*

Anxiety is experienced by all people and it makes its presence felt in varying degrees or at various levels. These levels depend of course upon factors surrounding each life and the way each person has or has not managed pressure, worry or stress. Imagine a colour wheel created to exhibit the many variations of fear and anxiety! If we could spin such a fantasy, we would see a spectrum of hues building from the pale dread of the prospect of an injection to the deeper tones of apprehension and foreboding and finally to black incapacitation, when people become totally consumed and ill, suicidal perhaps – all in fact, because of fear.

Though I will discuss it more fully later, it is important here to take a brief look at stress. People readily say that they are 'stressed out', or unwell because of stress. But I'd like to re-frame that assumption. 'Stress' is about our response to the demands of living – the difference between what is happening in our life and how we are handling it all. 'Stressors' are those things that are happening. The way we handle all those things can be either in a positive or negative manner. If we're positive about life's events, we won't feel stressed. But if overwhelmed by negativity, this is most certainly due to anxiety about whatever is going on. Unless we do something to manage that anxiety, it won't disappear of its own accord. Rather, untended, the anxiety level will increase. *That* is when we feel 'stressed'. So stressors are a trigger that may heighten anxiety and bring about the kind of discomfort we refer to as 'stress'.

Even more significantly, the level of anxiety being experienced also depends upon a person's level of nervous tension at any given time. If we're not handling the happenings in our life with ease, tension will increase. When tension rises, so also does anxiety – and vice versa and each reaction feeds the other. Nervous tension is in itself a negative coping strategy, familiar to many. It's not at all unusual, is it, to hear the cry: 'If only I could relax and unwind.' So anxiety, tension and stress are all intertwined and a pattern begins to form – for some people at least – where these reactions become a familiar part of daily life.

Our beginnings are always conditioned by individual upbringing, parental competence or incompetence, the influence of culture and religious interpretation, the general growing up environment, the helpful or unhelpful influence of teachers or mentors, the weight of the peer group, early life trauma and the many and varied factors that take place throughout the developing years.

Our perception of life is governed by all that conditioning – some of which of course, is stressful! Triggered by stress, *some* people – competent and strong people who are also of sensitive temperament, who have a busy mind, who are creative or imaginative in thought and usually also in tactile ways, who live to a large extent in their heads and who internalise worries and concerns — are likely to be more naturally anxious than others. If such people have also been significantly exposed to negative influences in early life, such a person may have gleaned an 'untrue' perception of themselves and their place in the world. If unduly pressured, worried or *stressed* such a person thus becomes a likely candidate for an anxiety disorder.

While anxiety, tension and stress are part of being human they can become excessive to the extent that people need relief – and desperately. To achieve that relief we need guidance, for unfortunately we are not usually taught to deal with these matters as students and such information is rarely handed down to us effectively by our elders. So we don't really know how to care for ourselves in this regard. When confused, frustrated, frightened and in need of direction, we either fight back with ever-increasing tension which exacerbates the problem, or we seek respite in dependency upon alcohol, cigarettes or drugs — always temporary, often destructive, and filled with the risk of leading to further distress.

One very common way of trying to fight anxiety, is the development of a phobia. As a *compulsion* draws people *towards* something, a *phobia* leads people *away from* something. Both begin as defences but neither, of course, is ultimately helpful – and that is why compulsions and phobias appear to become problems in themselves! History tells us that these expressions of anxiety have been suffered by people from time immemorial. But they seem uncommon because people fear discussing them. None of us likes to admit to fear of any kind, probably because of the fact that we are really afraid to be afraid! If fear and its effects are so widespread, why worry? Let's talk about it – let's open up the topic of fear and anxiety and explore its domain in a positive and constructive way.

When a person who is susceptible to anxiety experiences an attack of panic which is the result of escalating anxiety levels, he or she becomes extremely afraid. Panic is a greatly magnified 'normal' *flight or fight* reaction in which the physical symptoms of fear become intensified. Of course, at this initial attack, the person has no understanding of what is happening — except that his or her body is in great distress. Panic symptoms can include trembling, sweating, nausea, dizziness, chest pain, rapid breathing, heart palpitations or missed beats, breathing difficulties, and hyperventilation, numbness and tingling in the arms and hands, feelings of physical imbalance, visual disturbances, sensations of de-realisation or of being out of control and the possibility of loss of consciousness.

An episode of panic can create shock and it may even take several days for the reverberations of the experience to settle. In most instances, with some reassurance and the passing of time, the intense anxiety settles and the individual continues to resume a normal life.

But as already stated, anxiety doesn't just go away. Its presence lingers and high tension levels remain. For some people, other symptoms begin to appear. These notably include insomnia and exhaustion as the sufferer faces sleepless nights thinking about their health and 'that dreadful attack'. Worry dominates, tension increases more, the heart beat is heavy, awareness of the five senses is intensified, headaches are frequent, nausea returns, the throat feels constricted and the mind is on high alert. A sense of depression may envelop the sufferer along with alarming irrational thoughts, immense insecurity, non-specific dread and doubts as to one's sanity. The symptoms are obstinate, nothing brings relief and even if medication makes a difference, niggling reminder symptoms give rise to countless further fears. This scenario hints at a picture of the classic 'breakdown' which used to be spoken of in hushed tones. Better perhaps to see it as a 'break-through' where the possibility of self understanding and positive change is possible? But such vision cannot be contemplated – yet. The one desire is to lose the recurring symptoms and gain some 'normality' again.

So the person concerned begins to fight the symptoms and commences a defence against the possibility of another (panic) attack re-igniting them. I think it's really important to understand that anxiety reactions are not logical; they are not part of the conscious mind or of conscious action. Remember, the only indications that something is wrong are the awful recurring symptoms and the prospect of another panic attack. So, depending upon the greater or lesser degree of anxiety, defensive steps are taken in order to cope:

To relieve their anxiety, some will practice avoidance where specific situations are shunned. The result of this will be, for example, *claustrophobia or social anxiety disorder.*

Some will become obsessive, checking or touching or washing or counting relentlessly to relieve anxiety. The result of this will be *obsessive compulsive disorder.*

Some will experience other phobic defences or separation anxiety or a mix of all reactions.

Some will become depressed — in fact, most will become depressed — if only because of the incarcerated position of one kind or another in which they find themselves trapped.

Some of these reactions will be relatively mild and the sufferer can continue with life in a staccato sort of way. Some will be drastically severe and life becomes tarnished by this apparently unseen force.

And some will withdraw, perhaps become reclusive, staying close to home and security and the most-trusted person. The result of this will be *panic disorder* and in all probability, *agoraphobia.*

In agoraphobia the sufferer seems to experience all of the above reactions, rolled into one. In intense anxiety, he or she moves *away from* situations, avoiding any place, open or confined, where he or she feels at risk. He or she is also filled with a compelling need to cling to home and/ or the presence of an individual of close personal relationship. And even at home, the symptoms are ever-present, causing more and more anxiety. So the phobic 'defence' becomes habitual, a survival pattern leading to a life of extreme limitation. The inner misery of living this way is immense. Nothing appears to bring relief, and since 'cure' seems so elusive, feelings of hopelessness within the situation begin to dominate.

Ultimately, as you will discover, after my personal eight-year struggle, I overcame agoraphobia relatively quickly and very easily by learning to *let go* – as opposed to holding on and fighting my fear. Through a very specific form of meditation I gradually gained a relaxed approach to living, and found my symptoms disappeared as calmness replaced agitation and fear. It followed then that order and energy steadily returned, tasks became less arduous and problems less worrying because of increased serenity. Little by little, new confidence surfaced which led to a fresh enjoyment of life and the fulfillment of many dreams. This was my own experience. But I know it also from numerous others who have walked my walk, some of whom have generously shared their stories as you will read later.

Within my liberation, I discovered that gaining control over anxiety and conquering fear — of any kind — is quite a straightforward process — though apparently contradictory in some ways. With understanding, trust, practice, commitment and a degree of time, success is at hand. Some may balk at the prospect of more 'work' — but this is scant in comparison to years wasted in perennial fear, lack of understanding and the frustration of an anxiety disorder with an indefinite life of its own.

However, there is something else of which we must be aware. In seeking to conquer fear we must also accept that this involves growth and growth is not always easy. As things change for the better there may be challenges. There *will* be challenges! And decisions. And learning to discard in subtle or complex ways those unhelpful habits, or dependencies, ideas and ideals. Insights will be discovered as will be a clearer picture of who you really are! Seeking the self, searching for truth and living in the present moment are popular themes in today's positive psychology. These concepts may have become popularised now but in fact they are themes of ancient origin and they hold much wisdom; unavoidably you will meet these topics as things change. You will also see them within my recollections as I hope to impart some of the personal insights I gained as I developed my-*self* beyond that all-encompassing fear.

Most of all, when freed from fear you will have choices and opportunities that you haven't had for some time. Maybe there are further decisions to make. Perhaps even that is a relatively new experience? Maybe there are old issues to resolve . . . acceptance, forgiveness or letting go of past hurts? Maybe there is some loss to come to terms with or grief to sustain. Maybe there are new enterprises on the horizon to entice your interest and satisfy your gifts. And it's never too late for any of these developments! All this and more can unfold when we understand anxiety more fully, when we find the way to take control, when we have calmly and confidently set life on its course — and usually, when we find support through the experiences of others. So, having opened up the topic of anxiety, let's now begin our journey.

PART ONE

My Personal Encounter

Chapter 1

MY INTRODUCTION TO STRESS

A man who fears suffering is already
suffering what he fears.

Michel de Montaigne

From the time I could walk, I belonged to Nessa. She was the lady next door, middle-aged, childless and lonely. I filled a large part of her life, and she gave me treasures to cherish in my memory that only a child can receive. Together we lived in a dream world where the sun always shone and all stories had happy endings. We shared many things, and I was her pride and joy for as long as my mother and father lent me to her. But the greatest treasure we shared was her garden. She grew everything beautifully: neat rows of vegetables, separated by paths upon which I could walk if I was careful not to overstep and squash the lettuces; crisp little carrots and the peas nibbled straight from their fresh green pods. She cooked baby beet especially for me; and I remember well the pungent scent of runner beans as we picked them by the basketful. These all grew from seeds which she planted in trays covered with glass; she showed me the minute shoots and we watched their daily progress in those tiny hothouses.

There was an enormous fig tree which always seemed to be laden with fruit, and by the age of three I was familiar with the soft sweetness of ripe yellow loquats and the substance of their grotesque and silken stone. Her peach tree produced perfect fruit; so large, so ripe, soft creamy green on one side and blushing pink on the other. When one or two would fall into the cascade of ferns near the veranda, she used to tell me that the little people had dropped them there for me; and I believed her.

In front of the house she amassed all the annuals as each paraded in turn; heady perfumed purple stocks, brilliant orange soldier flowers, masses of starry forget-me-nots, sapphire irises and golden daffodils.

Then I even knew their botanical names. She introduced me to the habits of spiders and insects, and I learned to identify all the garden birds and the call each one made. Every birthday she presented me with a posy of my favourites, the Cecile Brunner roses; tightly bunched buds, coral pink in the centre, unfurling gently to the soft hue of a sea-shell. I still melt when I see 'fairy roses'.

But the best place in the garden was under my mayflower tree. Just a bush, the mayflower seemed to me then like a huge tree! This was our special spot, its welcoming arms sheltering a cave of soft green grass, where the sandwiches were eaten and the stories were told. Heavily perfumed, my mayflower boasted a myriad of tiny petalled flowers which, when Nessa shook the branches, would cover us both in a shower of miniature white confetti. And under that tree was security, joy and quiet stillness, interrupted only by our special conversations and the distant droning of summer bees.

Such was the tranquillity of Nessa's garden — without fear.

By the ripe old age of six or seven, my visits to the garden became less and less frequent as I became involved with being a schoolgirl, and outgrew my fantasy land. In those years I, like all children, began to experience fear: fears of the dark, of ghosts and 'bogey men'; fear of school teachers, of being alone. It was fears like those that would prompt me to go and visit Nessa. We would have a chat and some fresh cake and go out to the garden. And always I returned home free and happy.

We learn from fear, and we also learn to overcome those childish fears by a basic will to do so and, more significantly, by other distractions. Over and above my school work, I had a passion for painting and drawing and play-acting imaginative games, together with my young sister and as many of the neighbouring children as I could persuade to co-operate with me. Such activities readily dispel fear. So my childhood fears diminished and became only vague memories, later to be laughed about.

But fear is a human instinct, the first of the three great emotions: fear, love and anger. As we develop, our basic instinct of fear is replaced by the intellectual response of *anxiety*, which covers a multitude of human worries.

I had no fears from childhood, and my anxieties in the pseudo-sophistication of the teenage years varied from concern that one or both of my parents would die, to the state of the world in general. After leaving school, I embarked upon a secretarial career which led me into responsible positions. I enjoyed my work, and my home life was secure and happy. So, if I had any real anxiety at all in those years, it was typical enough, I think, of the anxious moments of immaturity.

In those years and into my twenties, I was very much involved with creative ambitions in the field of singing and the theatre. Such interests, I believe, have the effect of counteracting anxiety to a rather large extent. So the security I had known from Nessa's garden was transferred to the security of creativity, and the security that is born of friendships, camaraderie, sharing that creativity.

Of stress in life I knew very little. Then, a few months after my marriage, my father died suddenly of a heart attack. This was my first close encounter with death. I recall feeling at the time that I was not reacting as I would have predicted, had I ever stopped to think about it. It is interesting how one remembers things that are said in times of stress. I recall vividly how I answered the telephone and my mother, in distress, told me the bad news. Then she added: 'I'm sorry to bother you.' What a strange thing for her to say — why should she have been sorry to bother me? And I remember how it seemed that the people I passed in the street as I went to her were in another world — an unfeeling world — when my world had been stricken with the initial unreality of grief. It was many hours before I shed any tears.

As I was more or less available to take much of the responsibility for my mother, I found I was rather leant upon. I had to be strong for her, talk to people, make and drink endless cups of tea, help her with the necessary arrangements and think about her future. When I finally realised that my father had left our midst, it was with an even greater sadness, because only a few days before we had told him that I was pregnant. His longing for the grandchild that he was never to see was very great.

Life, as always, goes on. After the initial shock and disturbance, new patterns formed. But my husband and I now had my widowed mother to consider. And then to our further dismay, about one month later my father-in-law died after a brief illness. Here was more stress for us as a young couple, and another lonely mother to console.

Since our marriage, my husband had resumed his engineering studies and was attending many lectures each week. Both of us were also occupied at night in a small restaurant we had at the time. Although this arrangement ran fairly satisfactorily, it involved a great deal of hard work, long hours and lack of rest and relaxation. So we decided we should change this lifestyle by selling that business, embarking upon another one closely related to his new profession. We began to take steps in this direction and had some extra stress and worry when things did not go exactly according to plan.

Then came the worst shock of all. At three o'clock one morning we received a message that my husband's brother-in-law in his thirties, had suffered a heart attack and died immediately, leaving a young wife and six very young children. This news seemed unbelievable. We felt terribly inadequate. We were surrounded by suffering and it was impossible to give enough help to those who needed it. If I had been spared stressful experiences in my earlier life, I was certainly being given them now and in no small doses. I was very shocked by it all. Our personal joy, the baby that was due in four months time, was about the furthest thing from our minds.

Within the next two months, an uncle also died suddenly of a heart attack; my husband contracted a serious eye disease and for some time there was a risk that he would lose his sight; and my mother had a stroke and was hospitalised. And I still hadn't had time to buy a dozen nappies for the expected baby.

When November finally came and our son was born, we felt we had lived through a lifetime of change. In those last weeks we had even managed to sell the restaurant and move to a small flat, feeling relieved of all that had recently occurred and strong in the hope that our baby was a herald of happier times ahead. He certainly was; but at the same time, suddenly I was a mother. That fact brought new responsibilities and a busier life and, although exhilarating, here was a new kind of stress. Nevertheless, for the next few months some semblance of normality returned.

However, probably triggered by the responsibility of motherhood, general fatigue and the experience of real anxiety, I recall that I began to over-worry about certain things; vague things, which I had not thought of before, and which I can't even put into words now. But I know that behind those worries were the sudden deaths — the loss without warning — and new fears of illness and death.

I also remember feeling that the peace and happiness we had looked forward to in married life seemed continually to be threatened by something beyond our control. I felt ill-at-ease. Because we respond to happenings in our life in our own individual way, for me, the negative events – times of crisis really – which punctuated our early married life were stressful and were increasing my anxiety. The pace of my life had been mounting in that stressful manner and I was not equipped to handle it.

Before our daughter was born eighteen months later, two more close relatives had died suddenly; my mother-in-law had been taken ill; and, when our baby girl was only three weeks old, my own mother was incapacitated again, and once more needed me.

I remember feeling very tired all the time, and always rushed and edgy, but I didn't have time to stop to think about it. Older relatives were inclined to suggest occasionally that I was 'doing too much' and other vague statements, but I really didn't know what they meant by those remarks — and there was no alternative anyway. In any case, I believe that opting out will never overcome any burden that responsibilities may bring.

Through all these disruptions, I was still trying to settle into married life. Although many people do it, coping with two infants is hard work in itself, without all the preceding and accompanying worries we seemed to have had. There were constantly things to be done, and apart from filling the role of wife, mother and daughter, I was helping in our business, which meant that I had a pretty constant part-time job as well.

It seemed that pieces of me were required by many people and I felt a great personal burden of responsibility. The suddenness and substance of the demands with which I was faced cast a giant shadow on life at that time. It was no longer the 'bowl of cherries' that I had known before and a sense of threat and precariousness continually haunted me. I do not recall these activities with resentment; they were things that just simply had to be done, and to achieve it all I was living on hardly any sleep and lots of nervous energy. Unfortunately, I accepted that mounting tension as being normal – the only way to live. Many do, and it is a great mistake.

I had also made another mistake. I had abandoned something which meant a great deal to me; my ambition in the world of the arts. It seemed that with so much happening, there just wasn't enough time, and other priorities came first. So I had no escape from anxiety in the form of creative relaxation.

This account seems to paint a rather sombre picture of our marriage in those early years. That is not necessarily so. In between the worries were times of much happiness. But for me, personally, the anxiety was there — a cloud of uncertainty — of something lost or never found; and the sudden knowledge of too much stress and the inability to deal with it. Life had become difficult, and stress was taking its toll.

The statement made so long ago by Michel de Montaigne probably sums up exactly the way I felt at that time, as I began to experience the adverse effects of stress. I was afraid of suffering, but I didn't realise that I was in fact, right then, suffering what I feared. If de Montaigne made this observation as long ago as the sixteenth century, it would seem that we haven't progressed very quickly in learning to overcome such suffering during the last 400 years! For much of the suffering of life in today's world can be summarised in that one well-known word: stress.

To be alive is to have demands placed upon us. Stress is the effect of those demands, whether they are pleasant demands or the demands of suffering. We cannot prevent stress. As humans we are fragile and we must suffer; that is a fact of life. But without understanding, guidance and assistance, such suffering can be harder to endure.

Dr Hans Selye, who first used the word 'stress' in the 1940s to describe the wear and tear caused by life, writes:

> The soldier who sustains wounds in battle, the mother who worries about her soldier son, the gambler who watches the races, the horse and the jockey he bets on: they are all under stress.
>
> The beggar who suffers from hunger and the glutton who overeats, the little shopkeeper with his constant fears of bankruptcy and the rich merchant struggling for yet another million: they are also all under stress.

> No-one can live without experiencing some degree of stress all the time. You may think that only serious disease or intensive physical or mental injury can cause stress. This is false. Crossing a busy intersection, exposure to a draft, or even sheer joy are enough to activate the body's stress mechanism to some extent. Stress is not even necessarily bad for you; it is also the spice of life, for any emotion, any activity causes stress. But, of course, your system must be prepared to take it.

In layperson's language, I think we can understand the effect of stress through the parallel meaning of stress as it has always been used by engineers to describe the interaction of force and resistance. An engineering student is taught that a piece of steel will change shape under stress, and when that stress is removed the piece of steel will resume its original shape. When again subjected to a greater stress, it will react to that stress by stretching or bending more than it did the first time, but will return perfectly to its natural form when the stress is removed. And so on it goes, giving way and stretching under the stress in a perfectly elastic manner, always returning to its original form, until the point of stress is reached where the steel yields; it goes beyond its elastic limit and its form is changed and will not return to the original. It could be said that the steel is then permanently deformed. However, the essence of the material is unchanged, and with heat and human skill the steel can be reconstituted and brought back to its original shape, to perform in the same resilient manner as it did before it was stressed beyond its limit.

While we people are far removed from steel, we too have an elastic limit — and an enormous ability to cope with many demands of life before reaching that limit. But if we are not handling those demands with ease, stress will begin to have adverse effects upon us. However, the way stress will affect us, or the degree of stress required before we reach our elastic limit, will depend upon each individual's ability to cope with the demands placed upon him or her. What is stressful for one may not be so for another. Something that is an exciting challenge to one person may be a massive problem to the next. A busy life to one may be a very easy life to someone else.

Many people suffer severe stress from the effects of devastating illness, bereavement or personal heartbreak and withstand it very well. Others experience tragedy, disaster or violence. Many more know the stress that comes of poverty, deprivation, broken homes, unemployment. These are major problems, and strangely, taken singly, they are often the problems that we cope with best.

We can also know stress resulting from lesser demands. Stress can mean something as minor as a new day beginning with the alarm clock failing; to pressure from advertising, personal decision making, conflicts within relationships, dissatisfaction at work, poor communication, peer-group pressure, expectations of women (liberated or otherwise, there are still expectations), and pressure on men as a result of this situation.

Challenges come from external influences too, as we learn to integrate rapidly changing technologies, innumerable gadgets and the speed and pressure of modern environmental facilities. All these are marvellous to possess, but if we are not easily handling what is required of us personally, the mere fact of living in a digital age can add fuel to the fire of stress.

We can assume then, that when stress begins to cause us unease, our anxiety level has increased. So we begin to fight back with tension. We are living in fear of suffering and we begin to suffer what we fear as we reach our elastic limit.

The most common reactions to stress are the early symptoms of anxiety: fatigue, edginess and irritability, insomnia, headaches, palpitations and the many vague complaints which are generalised as 'only nervous tension'. Then there are more dramatic reactions. Sarah, who was involved in a severe motor accident where someone was killed, developed asthma, later attributed to the stress of that ordeal. Bill, who nursed his sick wife for several years developed severe depression — more than grief — after her death.

People seem to be more susceptible to infectious illnesses when under stress; it is said that their resistance is lowered. And these days it is widely held that stress is a precipitating factor in catastrophic illnesses such as cancer, heart attacks and strokes.

When under stress we can feel fragile and fatigued and thus we *fear* an inability to cope with all we have to do. So, again, we suffer what we fear as anxiety rises to meet that fear. It can be seen then that stress is a significant player in this aspect of the game of life.

And as it happened, one day 'out of the blue', shortly after we settled once more after having moved our little family into our own home, I experienced for the first time in my life an attack of panic. It seemed that this was what I had been anticipating. Something that alarmed me greatly and something that could not be explained, had finally struck. It was as if my worst fears had been realised. I felt that I was next on the threatened list!

Chapter 2

PANIC ATTACK! AND OTHER CONSEQUENCES

❧

Life is made up of marble and mud.

Nathaniel Hawthorne

It was a hot, steamy and overcast day, my head was aching and I was very tired. I remember it well. My daughter, who was only seven months old at the time, had cried all night, supposedly teething. My small boy, not yet two and rather adventurous, as most little boys are, had already been bathed twice before mid-day — once for covering himself and his baby sister in the black sandy soil from around the camellias and a second time for polishing the floor with the contents of a packet of cocoa while I was bathing the mud off the baby.

I was watching the clock, as I had to be at the doctor's surgery at a particular time to have stitches removed from my leg, where I had been bitten by a dog a week or so before. Then I had two business phone calls to delay me. I left the children to be minded, visited the doctor's rooms and then rushed back to collect the children, for the person minding them was only available for that hour. I remember thinking that I should have stopped to eat lunch, because the children had been given theirs earlier and it was by now close to the middle of the afternoon. But I had some business at the bank in the next suburb and had to be there before they closed. So, thinking that I would eat later, I organised the little ones into the car again, settled with the babysitter and rushed off once more.

It was as I was driving in rather heavy traffic that I suddenly experienced an unpleasant feeling of unreality. I felt a surge of alarm at this new experience. I remember vaguely thinking that perhaps I had not been concentrating very well on my driving, and almost wanted to pinch myself to see if I were dreaming.

This feeling of unreality, I learned later, is quite a common symptom of anxiety. However, not knowing that then, I became tense in an attempt to overcome that unpleasant feeling. I then realised that I was feeling extremely unwell. I was giddy and nauseated, my head was pounding, my vision was blurred and my heart was thumping in my throat — and I was still driving the car. I managed to park it and sat there for a few minutes, terribly aware of the fact that I was ill and away from home and I had two very young children with me.

By then, I was also feeling weak and faint, hot and cold and gasping for breath – *hyperventilating*, so I learned much later. This resulted in a *tetanic spasm* occurring, a phenomenon precipitated by hyperventilation and usually attributed to certain decreased calcium levels. This unpleasant experience begins with tingling in the fingertips which gradually leads to numbness in the hands and limbs, and which, in my ignorance at that time, I thought was the sudden onset of paralysis. With all those dramatic sensations happening and the predicament of being responsible for my children, I was convinced that I was dying or certainly being stricken with some dreadful disease.

The memory of the sudden deaths and illness in our family flooded my mind and somehow I stumbled, panic stricken, into a shop nearby. All I could say was that I needed help, and quickly, as my head swam with dark patches of fading consciousness. I must also have been the colour of a sheet, for I certainly caused some concern amongst the shopkeepers. I had alarmed them as well as myself, as they confirmed a couple of weeks later when I returned to say 'thank you'.

I didn't actually lose consciousness as some do in such circumstances, but my mind was swamped with panic and I was terrified. Panic is a word we have come to use fairly loosely in our vocabulary, but the real meaning of the word can only be appreciated by someone who has been through a complete *panic attack*. At that time what I was experiencing was a mystery to me — but I remember feeling threatened by a sense of urgency, and all my responsibilities seemed to crowd into my thoughts, in particular my two little children still out there in the car. It was a sensational and very frightening experience and I felt, in my confusion, that if I wasn't dying, I was about to lose control of my reason and actions.

As being in control is a very important aspect of well-being to human nature, a panic attack is a very unpleasant experience. No one likes to feel threatened in any way, least of all to have their composure threatened. But when one feels threatened by something unidentifiable, it is doubly difficult to accept. I pictured myself in all that confusion, being removed from the scene with absolutely no control over the situation, even to the extent of being unable to communicate. In hindsight, a classic experience of *loss of self.*

The people in the shop kindly came to my rescue, and to my relief the effects of the attack gradually passed. They also insisted upon taking me home and I was made to promise to have a thorough medical examination. The local doctor assured me that there was nothing seriously wrong, and that I was over-tired and run down. As he knew the stresses we had been under within the family during those years, he emphasised those and said that I just needed a good rest. He was inclined to insist jovially that my experience was just a simple faint due to fatigue, and he did not seem able to explain any of the unpleasant sensations I had experienced. The word 'panic' was not mentioned at all. Panic is defined by many as 'runaway anxiety'. I guess I had just been lucky until that time, for I had never experienced even *mild* panic, as many people do when under pressure. This was something new to me, and it was more than mild panic, so despite his reassurance I could not help worrying about my misadventure. The responsibility for my two young children increased this concern.

If the GP, or anyone whose knowledge I trusted, had been able to explain those strange feelings properly to me, I possibly would have not thought any more about the attack. But explanation was lacking, definition was vague, and the memory of that feeling of impending loss of control seemed to be imprinted on my memory with electrifying reality.

I wanted to know what had caused such an attack so that it could be prevented from happening again. The only answer forthcoming was the repeated phrase that I had nothing to worry about and that I was simply 'on edge'. I found this difficult to accept. How could being 'on edge' cause such a dreadful physical feeling of illness? I had never fainted in my life, nor had any illness apart from the usual illnesses of childhood. There didn't seem to be any guarantee that 'it' would not happen again, and I began to dread the possibility of another attack.

Anyone will react slightly to a strange or new sensation, and if a person is tense, those reactions will be magnified as anxiety rises. With increased anxiety, tension too increases further which produces more escalating anxiety and so begins an endless journey upon a merry-go-round of negative reactions.

In this I was no exception. Without realising that I was doing so, I became very watchful for any sign of the attack occurring again and I therefore became increasingly tense. Typically, within a few days, I experienced another attack; not so severe, but of the same pattern. That seemed to be confirmation of the fact that my 'illness', whatever it was, had come to stay.

The doctor's opinion was sought again. This time I really expected him to find some physical cause — it would almost have been some sort of relief if he had — but again his reply was: 'You are over-tired.' He prescribed Amytal tablets and told me to rest for a few days. I would have taken any course of action he suggested in order to prevent those unpleasant sensations so I took the tablets as directed and rested. The medication made me lethargic and the rest only gave me time to dwell upon what was happening to me. The memory of those attacks, particularly the fact that the first one had occurred in such a vulnerable situation, was there to stay. I tried to forget it, but it haunted me. I was a very conscientious mother — what if it should occur out in the street again? What would happen to my precious children?

As well as these worries, I still had an underlying fear that the doctor had missed something and that I might well have some serious illness. Modern living has, unfortunately I think, conditioned us to taking medicine immediately we feel unwell. Unless there is something very seriously wrong with us, we soon feel better. This is partly because the medication aids recovery, and partly because time heals and the illness disappears. At this stage of my predicament although I was taking the prescribed medication 'scary' symptoms keep reappearing. While I could admit that I was undoubtedly over-tired and 'on edge', I was quite oblivious to the constancy of my tension level. So I simply tensed myself more and more against whatever sensations arose.

Many people have become used to tensing or holding on to themselves as they attempt to allay discomfort of any kind. I, for one, was determined to fight and beat this, for I certainly did not want any more of those attacks, whatever they were. So to fight it I used, or rather misused, tension, and thereby did nothing to reduce my symptoms; in fact I only aggravated them.

As well as worrying about the situation, I had great difficulty describing my feelings. It seemed as if no-one to whom I spoke could really understand why I was worried. I felt apprehensive about going out of the house alone, and all the time I didn't know that it was the tension within me that was causing all my trouble. In fact, I was causing all those sensations myself!

My dear mother, who was not a relaxed person and whose health was not good at that time, offered her help while I rested. Unfortunately, she appeared to have no idea of the worry I was experiencing and only wished to disregard it. In doing so, she was inclined to reprimand me, pointing out the abundance of good things in my life — in truth I was far better off than many others! Though regretful in doing so, I began to avoid *her* company too, and the help she offered.

For everyone's sake, my husband arranged for a housekeeper for the rest of the week. That lady was at least eighty years old. She arrived enveloped in an enormous overcoat and her determined expression was only the more emphasised by the flat straw hat she wore firmly pinned to the prim knot of grey hair on top of her head. These garments were shed as she swept through to my kitchen with intimidating efficiency, while at the same time appraising the situation.

'What's the matter with you?' she asked disbelievingly. I mumbled something vague about being told to take it easy and I could see that she was not impressed. For when you are in your twenties, unless you've just had a baby or a miscarriage, you are not of very great interest to most members of that brigade of housekeepers.

'It's probably sunstroke,' she concluded with an air of finality, wielding a broom.

She didn't drink tea or coffee or eat lunch, and rather reluctantly prepared something for me and the children, whom she obviously terrified. And she'd never been ill — in fact she'd never had a day off work in sixty years. I remember feeling slightly amused at the situation as I watched an eighty-year-old lady beating my rugs against the veranda post with as much vigour as if she had been driving a stake through the heart of a vampire. I didn't think I could stand this for a week.

Yes, perhaps she was right — maybe it was sunstroke! I decided I could get by without her and her daunting presence. The best way to have things the way you want them is to do them yourself and this ridiculous resting was certainly getting me nowhere.

The most practical thing to do was to ask my doctor to refer me to a specialist for a second medical opinion, and thereby, hopefully, alleviate all my worries. My doctor's philosophy was: 'It takes a long time to become run-down, so naturally it will take a long time before you feel yourself again.' I felt confused and rather angry that he could seem to treat this so lightly. Only a week or so before, I was — I thought — completely carefree, and now I felt that my security had crumbled. After all, what is a 'long time'? At twenty-six years old, I felt he seemed to be speaking of the rest of my life.

I was sent to a city physician and remember that visit with great clarity. Because I was feeling so insecure and I would not go alone, my husband accompanied me there, and patiently read a wearied *National Geographic* in the waiting room. The doctor was a rather supercilious man who wore a dark pin-striped suit in the heat of the Melbourne summer. His disdainful attitude had the effect of making me feel exceedingly foolish and inferior. We probably suffered a personality clash. In other words, there was no line of communication and certainly no empathy between us as doctor and patient. But he was supposed to be an expert, and I needed his advice.

I related my story, and his answers to my questions were directed at me as though I were about ten years old. His final diagnosis, after a thorough medical examination and much vague discussion, was that there was nothing the matter with me, and I had nothing to worry about, but it would probably be a good idea to continue to take medication for a while. He handed me a prescription for the Amytal I had already been prescribed. I was ready to accept any advice to be free of this 'illness', but real explanation was still lacking. I was still none the wiser as to what was causing the wretched symptoms or why I really needed Amytal. Even then, as he showed me out the door and saw my husband waiting for me, he commented: 'Well, you really didn't need protection; we're not such ogres, you know.' I think my mouth fell open in amazement. This was the very reason for my visit! Could nobody understand?

It is curious how circumstance alone can tip the scales of life one way or another. It is often amazing how an opinion expressed by the right person at the right time, or the wrong person at the wrong time, can influence our lives so much. At this point of my life, a set of circumstances arose without which I might never have developed agoraphobia.

After my visit to the physician, I made up my mind to forget the whole thing and get on with living. At least his opinion had put to rest any fear of serious illness, and without that worry and with the continuing medication, the symptoms — and my apprehension — subsided. I began to get back into the swing of life.

I took my mother and my two children on a short holiday. My husband remained in Melbourne so I had no fear then of being away from home. While my mother found the small children a little too tiring, we got on well and it was relaxing; a complete change. I enjoyed it and benefited from it without any symptoms of my former problem.

A few weeks later, my husband and I drove interstate to attend a wedding at which he was to be best man. At this stage, as I very much disliked taking tablets of any kind, and as I felt the whole matter was behind me, I discarded the medication. We left the children with relatives and this should have been a marvellous break together. Instead, it was a disaster.

Apparently my state of tension increased again. During the wedding, while seated separately from my husband, I once again began to experience the unpleasant feelings which had formerly threatened me. Not only was 'it' happening again, but 750 kilometres away from home. My mind was racing frantically with fear of another of those attacks occurring here, of all places, in the middle of somebody's wedding. Thankfully, the sensation passed without that happening but, of course, once more I began to be afraid. Because I was afraid, naturally I was tense, and throughout the rest of the holiday I was pursued by 'reminder symptoms' which were, to say the least, spoiling the holiday for both of us.

In desperation, I foolishly consulted a doctor in the city in which we were staying. This was the contretemps. I made a bad choice, for he was the type of man, as I later learned, who had the mentality of 'operating first and finding out what was wrong later'. With that in mind I'm only pleased that I didn't go to him with severe pain anywhere! However, he became very excited about the fact that, in his opinion, the symptoms I described — pounding heart, giddiness, and faintness — were consistent with those of a serious kidney ailment. At the same time, he more or less derided any treatment I had already received. In all, that was an opinion I could have done without, for yet another relative was, at that time, hospitalised with a terminal kidney disease.

All this brought about a sea of confusion and was utterly the last straw. I was a very worried young woman. I could not wait to get back home. The holiday had been an absolute waste of time and I began to miss my children dreadfully.

In a final attempt to add some interest to an otherwise incredibly introspective holiday, my husband decided he would distract me from my worries by taking an alternative route home to show me a part of outback Australia. Now, I'm a dreadful navigator at the best of times, but in my state of tension and worry I read the map upside down and it wasn't long before we were well and truly lost on an unmade road, somewhere beyond the proverbial 'black stump'. Naturally the car, which was not too functional anyway, broke down and could only be driven at walking pace until we eventually found a person (or perhaps a sheep!) for directions. We were then obliged to spend two days in that remote place while the car was repaired. I was absolutely sick with worry and was sure I would never see my beautiful children again.

When we eventually arrived home, I immediately went to my own doctor again and told him of my experience while on holiday, and the opinion of the doctor whom I had consulted there. His response was: 'Rubbish.' Once again I went through the whole medical examination routine. Once again I was proclaimed completely fit, and told not to worry. Unfortunately, that is often easier said than done.

Now I was really in a dilemma. My confidence was shaken; I wanted to believe my own doctor, but I was being pursued by those mysterious symptoms which I believed would culminate in that dreadful attack. And no-one seemed able to explain why.

Without fail, every time I began to venture out of the house, especially unescorted, and sometimes when with my husband, the symptoms would arise. As soon as I found myself alone in someone else's home, in the shopping centre, or driving from one place to another, I would begin to notice what I believed to be the onset of 'the attack'. Suddenly and unaccountably my heart would begin to pound, my palms would sweat, I would begin to feel lightheaded and fear that I might faint; and the feeling of panic (as yet un-named) would begin to well up within me. That would be the moment when I would rush to my car, or out of the shop, or abandon any purpose for being there and make for home and safety. Each time this happened, of course I unknowingly submitted to fear and reinforced the problem. With later experience and understanding it became easy to see how those symptoms of fear had me completely bluffed. But I felt then as though I were being followed by some unidentifiable illness which overtook me whenever I was out of the house.

I began to dread leaving home where the whole frightening experience would be repeated and I was very much afraid of those attacks – whatever they were. As no-one else could help me control this recurring 'illness' I somehow felt that by avoiding the situations which apparently caused 'those attacks', I could prevent them from occurring. So I began to remain at home – using avoidance as a coping strategy.

As the symptoms of the attack I dreaded could occur anywhere at all beyond my front gate – and at times inside it – I began to avoid *any* situation in which I felt an attack could occur. The more I tried to forget it, the more the memory of the first occasion persisted. And each time I anticipated an attack, I felt certain that this would be the time when it would wholly engulf me and deal its final blow.

Without knowing that I was doing so, without real awareness of my level of tension, I was drawing upon it constantly as I fought to avert any hint of the symptoms. I was guarded and apprehensive, waiting for 'it' to pounce on me. With such an attitude pervading my life it was understandable that I preferred to remain safely at home.

As time went on and I remained tense and anxious, the *habit* of avoiding the feared situations became more firmly fixed. And sure enough, the unpleasant symptoms of fear which I thought to be the onset of sudden physical illness would strike whenever I ventured out. I had become conditioned, like the famous Pavlov's dogs, to expecting that reaction to occur. In fact, sometimes the symptoms would be provoked simply by the knowledge that I had to leave the house.

I felt ashamed of myself for what seemed to be a preoccupation with my health and to try to explain such a senseless fear to others was embarrassing. So as well as fighting the symptoms I unwittingly kept my distress alive by increasing tension still more to *hide* my fear. There was no satisfactory medical explanation, the treatment I resumed made no difference and I felt confused, frustrated, saddened and alone.

Stress had caused me anxiety, which led me to become acquainted with the symptoms of fear – those responses of fight or flight which are the body's preparation to meet some emergency. The only emergency, had I known it then was my fear of being overwhelmed by my own natural response to danger. But no; I was innocently trapped by my own reactions.

Had anyone suggested to me before that time that I would ever develop a phobia I would have believed they were joking. As for being afraid to leave my home and thereby be deprived of so many of the things I enjoyed in life, I would not have believed that possible.

How little I understood then of fear, of people, of life!

Chapter 3

FEAR AND PEOPLE

❦

Why do we feel embarrassed, impatient, fretful, ill at ease,
Assembled like amateur actors who have not been
assigned their parts?

T.S. Eliot, The Family Reunion.

What a magnificent description of all our human insecurities: scratch
the surface and uncover fear, hiding under the guise of more acceptable
reactions!

'Embarrassed' – those times when people are so sensitive to the complications of life that they overreact in self-conscious confusion and distress. Worried (or fearful) that they have said or done something out of
line, or that they are unable to reach self-imposed standards or meet the
satisfaction of others, people retreat and communication is lost. And
how frequently are the young embarrassed by continual criticisms or, on
the other hand, the praise of doting parents?

'Impatient' – the modern world is filled with impatience. One of the
most frequent statements heard today is 'there isn't enough time'. The
pace of life becomes faster with every passing year (and every new inven-
tion) and the emphasis of success is often heavily laid on how quickly
things can be achieved; from worldwide communication in an instant
down to soft boiled eggs in the microwave. And so, it is not easy to sit
still, difficult to pause for quiet conversation, hard to listen when others
are speaking, impossible to bear solitude, and even more impossible to
relax. Fear that we cannot absorb it all, or cope effectively keeps a sense
of impatience alive and denies the ability to savour the glorious moments
of each day of our life.

'Fretful' – now that's an interesting old-fashioned word, from 'fret',
primarily meaning worry. I learned recently from a friend that his mother used the word *fretmarked* to refer to people whose lives had been difficult because of the kind of events which today we would categorise as

'stress'. Though it carries overtones of a label, I like the word because of its ability to determine something specific where 'stress', by comparison, is a very loose or open-ended term. To fret is to worry and worry relates to fear.

'Ill at ease' – the understandable result of embarrassment, impatience and fretfulness wearying and burdening people with tension, edginess, the 'jitters' and lack of relaxation, the way people can feel because of the subtle influence of fear.

These reactions, familiar to all I think, are largely based on the one question we all want answered: *what do you think of me?*

We all want the answer to be positive and continually *fear* that it will not be. We fear rejection – said to be the greatest human fear of all. We fear openness and contact with others and the closeness of relationships, and yet we fear the misery of loneliness. People crave acceptance, wanting to be well thought of by others and to give an appearance of capability and harmony with life. But while our contentment is clouded by fear and all its surrounding reactions, it can be hard to get our act together. In striving to exist – like Eliot's actors – all too often people assemble, waiting and wondering who or what they really are.

Although we wear our masks quite well, insecurity, or fear, is expressed in many other subtle ways. Defensive stances may cause people to retreat, or to become too assertive, or too shy, to become too obliging, to display aggression, to become comic or over-effusive, to exude indifference or to openly patronise or offend.

These reactions become part of individual style and form what we know as our personality — or ego, really. And at times, if fear is the dominant control in personality development these defensive reactions become so distorted as to lead to difficulties in relating to others. These are the ways the human condition as a whole can be largely influenced by fear.

But fear is not readily expressed for we are inclined to believe that fear is something we should not feel, possibly out of fear of rejection – and so we tend to conceal our fears. It is therefore probable that those whom we may envy for their apparent confidence are struggling with inner fears, just as the rest of us.

Despite a common disinclination to admit to fear, we need to understand that it can serve a useful purpose, too.

In primitive times, parents had to teach children to be on guard for wild animals, enemy tribes and similar dangers. They would also have been taught which food was safe to eat and which was not, how to defend themselves if required, places that were safe and unsafe to traverse, and countless other aspects of self-preservation. Doubtless only those who respected fear were the survivors, so life would have been filled with fear. The human race has surely survived thus far through the asset of its innate fear!

As civilised people, while we no longer risk attack by wild animals, we still need our instinctive fear. For their own safety, we must continue to teach our young to respect danger and act accordingly. But real fear in civilised society is not generally experienced unless we are unusually threatened. If confronted by a dangerous person wielding a weapon, we would be very much afraid, and rightly so. We might be able to scream. Or we might try to defend ourselves – either physically or by verbally reasoning a way out of our plight. Or we might run from the situation or contrive another escape. There would certainly be feelings of panic but in the face of visible danger the body's response would convert to action. Adrenaline and other hormones would be released by the amygdala, that tiny part of the brain that reacts especially to fear. And consequent physical responses such as increased heart rate, breathing, blood pressure and blood flow would fire up the autonomic nervous system and boost performance at a time of need – the fight or flight response to emergency.

In an unusual situation such as that, the fear reaction would be a very reasonable emotional and physical response. But with our innermost fears, those we are unable to clearly determine, there is no action to be taken and the body's natural mechanism converts to anxiety where a panic attack is probable.

As explored a little earlier, anxiety is experienced at some level by all people – those times where we feel embarrassed, impatient, fretful and ill-at-ease – and more. We are complicated beings and we become anxious about a great many things. But when there is no outward foe to meet, we are often perplexed by these mysterious, anxious reactions. The 'bottom line' though, is always fear!

Failure can mean different things to different people, and it is not unusual to fear the devastation and shame of failure, whatever that may mean to us as individuals. Some fear success, and will retreat when just about to reach their goals. We fear being hurt, either emotionally or physically, and we fear the vulnerability of mutual trust. Many people fear responsibility, particularly the responsibility of parenthood. Others, who are already parents, will fear that their children will be less than perfect and so they fear disappointment in that regard. People, especially the young, fear that if they do not conform to the modes of behaviour set by their peers, they will no longer be accepted – another form of rejection. We fear appearing foolish to others, and many are timid and afraid even to cross a floor or enter a social situation unfamiliar to them. We fear loss of worldly possessions and fear that somehow others can take what we have from us. Some will fear any kind of risk and some have the sad fear of growing older, a privilege denied many.

We are not born with these fears; like all our learning, they come with our environment. Many people carry the fears of their parents for a lifetime and some can metaphorically perish from lack of living, due to fears imposed upon them by overprotective elders. Fears are transferred almost without our knowing, such as in the case of women who dread childbearing for fear of pain. Many modern women (and indeed men) become burdened by fear as new roles dispense with precedents which spelled security. People carry with them inherited fears and compulsions surrounding fear of contamination, of germs, animals, reptiles, spiders and insects, of drowning or injury from the elements of nature. Others express their fear in superstitions regarding colours, numbers and so on, or become reliant upon lucky charms, rituals or other crutches to lessen their uneasiness. Even the least of these nagging fears can be restrictive to happy living.

There are also those fears which seem very surprising. A friend confided that she would usually prefer to spend a day alone rather than contact someone for company. She is too afraid of intruding. Another such instance is that of an older lady with a fear of using the telephone. It is a 'modern' device and she fears it. No hope for her as a PC whizz? Yet she has proved on a couple of occasions that she has no fear of tackling a burglar.

Today, fear surrounds issues such as global warming, threats to wold peace and claims as to the cause of various illnesses: while certainly the consideration of one's eventual death and the unknown is cause for many to fear. And fear is frequently found among the elderly, who can feel threatened by the pace of living and the dread of responsibilities they believe are beyond them as their own lives draw towards evening.

If we are at ease within our life, most of these fears do not linger, disappearing with satisfying occupation and rational thinking. But if we are not at ease, *anxiety* will rise. Our brain has to deal with a lot, doesn't it? Like an inbuilt skein of tangled yarn, fear and anxiety affect us all and circulate within the society in which we live. Unless informed otherwise, we give it to ourselves, we give it to others and we receive it back. This contagious effect of anxiety upon society is accentuated through the ready availability of sensationalism. Today's technology opens doors to information never known before and the media relies heavily upon dramatic stories to sell its wares, popular themes being those of tragedy and illness. Artists and creators express the signs of culture and a history of the society they represent. Unfortunately too many of our popular songs, poetry and prose reflect issues of sadness, loneliness, isolation and *fear* – contributing to worry, introspection and therefore increased anxiety and depression. Only the fortunate who have discovered peace of mind or 'personal transformation', or those who are naturally relaxed, or especially placid (or far less sensitive) can avoid the unfortunate consequences of anxiety.

As mentioned earlier, all this anxiety produces increased nervous tension. Nervous tension appears in the habits which we adopt in order to relax. We see tension in impatient or agitated behaviour, an inability to slow down, or ever-increasing irritability which might prompt a visit to the doctor for sedatives. People will say that they're always tired, can't cope, can't sleep, feel tense all the time and are always in a hurry. Tension causes overreactions to happenings in life in which people feel edgy and distracted. Or the symptoms of tension are often experienced in physical sensations when we become involved in a particular incident – a heated argument at home or in business, or a close encounter with a motor accident. Our heart will thump and we will feel weak and say that we are shaken or that our nerves are on edge – while reaching for another whisky …

When stress comes along in some form or another, people's anxiety is naturally increased and so, as I did, they generate more nervous tension – a perfect trio of ingredients for *symptoms* of anxiety to eventuate. For some, these may be visible in physical ailments such as high blood pressure or a stomach ulcer. Nervous rashes, allergic reactions, migraine headaches and a wide range of psychosomatic illnesses can all be related to stress and accompanying anxiety and tension.

And if, for some, these reactions are centred in the emotions and the nervous system, it is at such a time that a *phobia* is likely to arise. As we all learn neurotic trends, likes and dislikes, habits and quirks that sneak into our personalities, phobias, too, are learned. A phobia, it seems, arises from fear experienced when the anxiety level is higher than usual. A phobia appears to provide the individual with a kind of defence – or protection – against whatever is feared. But as we can see, fear feeds upon fear, and as humans instinctively fight fear, it is not long before the phobic reaction is no longer useful but detrimental to well-being.

Some therapists maintain the opinion that fears and phobias usually represent anxiety experienced in early childhood or adolescence; possibly an association with the hurt of being punished for an offence not committed, jealousy at the arrival of another sibling, anger at being left alone, or possibly some deeper, more traumatic experience such as physical or sexual abuse. Such themes can certainly contribute to explanation, and yes, the influences of early life are extremely powerful and *can* provide valuable insight into adult responses. But from the very large number of people who have fears and phobias, obviously the incident which may initially have caused anxiety does not necessarily have to be of great significance. Suffice to say that every child knows anxiety at some time – and any one of a thousand incidents could potentially trigger panic in adult life – which makes the search to identify a single such incident rather like looking for a needle in a haystack.

In exploring fear it is important to recognise that there is nothing unnatural about fears and phobias and that these reactions can be mild or moderate or severe. Fear is not necessarily a sign of psychological weakness or lack of stamina. Again, fear is our natural human protection from danger. It is, however, the way our intellect has adapted fear in the form of anxiety that can greatly inhibit the enjoyment of life.

We all know of big strong men who dread a visit to the dentist or who will faint at the sight of a hypodermic needle; or the much-caricatured women who faint when they see a mouse. These are examples of phobias that are easily accepted though they still produce sweating palms, nausea and weakness, thumping heart – the physical symptoms of anxiety.

The most well-known of all phobias is claustrophobia in which the individual feels trapped, closed in and out of control. It is very common to experience claustrophobia in theatres, in elevators or among large crowds of people. Many cannot face going into a church, driving through a tunnel or taking a trip on an underground train.

Acrophobia is another common phobia, where people cannot tolerate heights – any sort of heights ranging from step ladders to bridges to tall buildings. One man explained that heights raise a fear that he might impulsively throw himself over the edge. The common fear of flying reaches phobic proportions for many and is usually expressed as a combination of claustrophobia and acrophobia. Other common phobias include fear of eating in public places, sometimes related to the fear of food or of choking or being under some kind of public scrutiny.

There is an unusual story with a touch of pathos told to me by an old lady. Hers was a phobia about taking a bath. As a young woman back in the 1930s she was in hospital awaiting the birth of her child. For some reason the nursing staff insisted upon her taking a hot and very deep bath, as she said 'right up to my neck'. With the imminence of the birth and her general anxiety this was an occasion of terror. She recalled it years later with as much fear and aversion as if the incident had taken place only yesterday.

Another woman recalled a childhood memory of trying to play with what she saw as a cuddly kitten. This kitten turned out to be a rather snarley ageing cat, which hissed, bared its teeth and flung out a paw with claws released, ready to fend off this human nuisance. The child screamed, riveted to the spot as tears streamed down her cheeks. Her mother, overreacting, rushed to the child to rescue her, while old puss went back to sleep. After all that commotion, the girl had a lasting memory of fear in association with cats – and cat-phobia lasting a lifetime.

While people with specific phobias find these to be inconvenient at times, most can be lived with and negotiated by avoiding the anxiety producing situation. But *agoraphobia* is likely to be more severe in intensity and somewhat more complex.

Dictionaries often define agoraphobia as a 'morbid fear of being in open or public spaces' – but this interpretation is inadequate. Certainly the person with agoraphobia may well dread open or public spaces but most will also dread closed areas or restriction of any kind – any place at all really where he or she may feel anxious – particularly if unaccompanied by a person in whom he or she deeply trusts.

Wikipedia on the net describes agoraphobia more broadly as:

> a condition where the sufferer becomes anxious in environments that are unfamiliar or where he or she perceives that they have little control. Triggers for this anxiety may include crowds, wide open spaces or travelling, even short distances. This anxiety is often compounded by a fear of social embarrassment, as the agoraphobic fears the onset of a panic attack and appearing distraught in public.

Similarly, from a diagnostic perspective, the DSM-IV[1] criteria states that agoraphobia is experienced as

> anxiety about being in places or situations from which escape might be difficult (or embarrassing) or in which help may not be available in the event of having an unexpected or situationally predisposed panic attack or panic-like symptoms. Agoraphobic fears typically involve characteristic clusters of situations that include being outside the home alone; being in a crowd or standing in a line; being on a bridge; and travelling in a bus, train or automobile.

[1] Diagnostic and Statistical Manual of Mental Disorders, 4th ed. American Pyschiatric Publishing Inc.

From these latter sources we can conclude that agoraphobia might be identified as *the fear of leaving the safety of home.*

But there's even more. While agoraphobia seems to relate to the avoidance of panic and certain environments, for the majority of sufferers the condition becomes further complicated by the fact that unlike other phobias, the triggers appear to be extremely random; the fear does not relate to any tangible or visible object. As with all anxiety reactions, intensity can vary from mild to moderate to severe. For most agoraphobics it is usually so severe, so generalised, so limitlessly over-lapping of other anxiety reactions that, at any time or place, the victim may be alerted to overwhelming physical distress. And, even more alarming still, as well as physical symptoms, as indicated earlier, there is mental anxiety where thoughts become rapid or snatches of bizarre thought may occur. Sometimes these include fear of self-harm or of harming another and these moments are very 'scary'. Or the opposite may occur, where the mind feels dull and empty. These reactions are not related to depression or the serious consideration of such acts – they are a kind of mimic coming from the tired, stressed, hyper-vigilant mind in which perceptions are temporarily awry. To try to explain these moments of fearful thought to others without sounding completely 'loopy' is very difficult and over recent years I have had occasion to reassure many that these too, are symptomatic of the high anxiety experience. The mind is so powerful … we rely on our mind so much and take its flow for granted. But when fear seems to have penetrated our all, and confusion reigns supreme, to be left alone with our mind can be another terrifying prospect. Hence – the agoraphobic may feel fully out of control and his or her need for constant company, support and security is paramount.

It must be understood that being agoraphobic does not mean that the victim is afraid of 'a shop' or 'a street' or 'an elevator'. If this phobia could be attached to something identifiable, it would be relatively simple to accept and live with it. But the agoraphobic cannot identify or accept this fear and feels constantly frustrated and threatened by something unknown. On a good day and in apparently secure surroundings, the phobia may appear to be forgotten until, having to face the prospect of stepping outside that door, he or she can be swamped with debilitating symptoms. So being outside of home is the closest one can come to recognising what is feared, rationally, the best thing to do is avoid being out there!

By the same token, being agoraphobic does not necessarily mean that other *full* phobic reactions will be regularly experienced. An agoraphobic man told this humorous story. He and one of his mates went on an historical visit to a cemetery. The agoraphobic felt safe because he was in the company of his friend but in their enthusiasm, the two were separated. On seeking his friend for support he found him petrified with fear and expecting to see a ghost as he had come upon an old grave with an open tombstone. The agoraphobic man calmed the other by saying: 'Don't you worry about that, the dead won't hurt you ... for me it's just being alive anywhere that's scary!'

So in agoraphobia there is no single identifiable object or clearly defined situation to avoid – just an ever-present insecurity where the outcome of fear is feared. It can be seen I hope, that this level of anxiety is powerful and reaches beyond clearly defined limits. Therefore to keep the growing understanding of agoraphobia as simple as possible, at this point I prefer to say:

Agoraphobia is the fear of fear.

Since overcoming this condition myself, and having had so much experience with other sufferers, before, during and after their healing, I have found people whose lives have been impaired in this way for up to forty years. The state of fear can vary from total enclosure to a finely tuned life where certain boundaries govern existence. In very severe cases, the victim will remain within the home, never going anywhere. The majority can make short distances to safe destinations and can only go further afield in the company of another (husband, wife, partner or parent) in whose confidence they trust.

Managed in the ways that people deal with all phobias, the agoraphobic is superficially living like anyone else. But constantly negotiating fear by these means causes him or her to endure a second-class existence to say the least.

Most agoraphobics do not accept their condition and are constantly striving to overcome it and live as fully as they did before fear began to dominate their lives. This striving builds strength and discipline. Such a person is very likely to be the one who will act very responsibly in a crisis, and is well prepared to withstand with good judgment, any other troubles that life may deliver. But because the development of the fear of fear is so restricting to individual freedom, and people become servants to fear, their lives are virtually no longer their own. This effect puts tremendous strain on family, friends and colleagues and a great deal of patience and understanding from these supportive people is required.

The agoraphobic is largely just like anyone else apart from one difference: in wanting so much to overcome the problem, that person is ever fighting, and therefore innocently prolonging their misery indefinitely.

That's how I found myself in that summer of the 1960s. I should have been at a peak of happiness and security. Instead, I seemed to be very much like one of Eliot's actors – on the stage of life waiting for guidance, wanting to grasp the situation and terrified to make a move.

Chapter 4

LIVING WITH FEAR

❧

Who overcomes by Force hath overcome but half his foe.

Milton

The telephone woke the entire household one night and the clock read 2.30 a.m. The strident bell had penetrated every-one's dreams, but when it was answered the caller hung up. Each of us looked at the others help-lessly. The surge of alarm that filled our hearts in those few minutes of awakening was far from pleasant; the thoughts and fears and questions as to why someone should be telephoning at that hour caused temporary anxiety. And I momentarily experienced a stab of fear reminiscent of many years before.

Everyone has experienced at some time the piercing fear that hits us and then sweeps through us when faced with something alarming or something we dread having to do. In my years of agoraphobia, those moments were with me every time I was faced with leaving the house. And from that first flush of fear would arise all the other unpleasant symptoms: pounding heart, giddiness and weakness. As those symptoms mounted in intensity, the anticipation of loss of control of the situation was there, and with that came the even greater fear of how, or if, I would cope if that occurred. I use the words 'loss of control' because it was not until many years later that I learned that the feeling I lived in dread of was, in fact, panic.

The more I remained at home in my attempt to avoid the possibility of those attacks and in trying to control the persistent symptoms which, as yet, I didn't understand, the more difficult it was to go out. Knowing that there were certain events which had to be attended and could not be avoided would cause much worry, and rarely was I at ease in any situation away from home. However, as my husband and I both enjoyed the company of others and participating in as many things as possible, I usually managed to force myself to go anywhere, as long as he was with me and never far out of sight. Occasionally fear would overcome me to the extent that I could not go through with whatever it was we had to do, but this didn't happen too often on occasions where we were both involved. Just being present was however, still an enormous strain.

Unfortunately, fear was a constant presence when I was alone. I was able to travel comfortably for a mere kilometre from home, providing I drove myself, I was out for as short a time as possible and my car was always parked close at hand. To achieve this, I often had to take the pre-scribed medication, which I greatly disliked having to do. I only ever took very minimal doses and when absolutely necessary. Even then I always, at some stage of my journey, experienced the onset of the symptoms of panic. The complete attack never occurred again (for all my worrying), but the anxiety symptoms were with me like a constant reminder that 'it' had not forgotten me. Those would be the times when I would abandon my purpose for shopping or escape to home from some social situation, relieved that I had survived.

In striving to deal with all this, I next developed an aversion to my car, laying blame on it for producing the dreaded symptoms. So I per-suaded myself that a car was not essential to my day-to-day requirements and we sold it. Strange, really – because driving was one of my passions and I have always been a confident and competent driver. But having no car was a perfect excuse not to have to participate in trips away from home alone and, if necessary, at that stage of my fear, I could still take public transport. I secretly hoped that by disposing of the car I would also dispose of my symptoms – as did one man who simply gave his car away for the same reason.

Home was obviously my base as the mother of our young children but it seemed necessary despite my lingering fear, that I try to achieve at least one small trip beyond 'safety' each day. This was my husband's encouraging idea and so I disciplined myself to attempt anything in a bid to conquer my apprehension. Knowing that it was better to continue to try and succeed just a little than not at all, I persevered, hoping that one day I would find myself miraculously free again. However, my successes became fewer and fewer and I would always experience some of the unpleasant sensations, frequently returning home shaken and distressed.

I should also say here that being at home was not always a 'walk in the park' either – ah … an interesting pun! When anxiety rages at that level, its' presence is constant. It's just a little easier and more comfortable and holds less risk of embarrassment if those uncontollable feelings occur at home!

So then I *would* go to the park. I would take the children for walks within the block in which we lived, or to the small shopping centre nearby. I avoided open areas or playgrounds, where my active little boy would want to stop for ages on the swings, or simply just run in open space. The intensely anxious person feels extremely alone and open to threat in spacious areas, whether it be in parkland, streets or freeways, the vastness of a beach or the seemingly oppressive atmosphere of the mountains. Space becomes visually surreal and there appears to be no hope of gathering oneself for escape in an open area if the feelings of panic begin to arise, so I stuck firmly to a very restricted walk.

At the same time, friends in the neighbourhood with children the same age as mine offered mutual companionship for the little ones. But, much as I desired it, I began to find it difficult to visit their homes. Different from open space, but bringing the same intensity of fear, is the confinement of closed areas, so great is the tension against which we are fighting. Of course, we do not understand this at the time. Under those conditions, the response of fear can be precipitated by the mere closing of a door in an unfamiliar house, similar to a feeling of being trapped while waiting to be served in a shop. So I felt really secure only in my own home and I was very happy to have a constant stream of small visitors to play with my children there. What was more, I didn't have to go far afield to provide that company. Our street was pleasant and safe. The houses were not too far apart and the neighbourhood was well endowed with small children to play together. I was also fortunate that compromise was easily reached — I didn't have to go much further than my front gate to safely return some or collect my own.

In that more comfortable space, I found many ways to keep occupied. I was still involved in our business, and worked at my part in it from home. I also maintained as many interests as possible without having to leave the house. Having accepted that I could no longer pursue my singing ambitions, I had a yearning to study art seriously, but I could hardly expect my husband to accompany me to classes or lectures. That was out of the question. I did attend ceramic classes nearby and, once I had forced myself to get there, found that potting and moulding is creative and good fun. But, as usual, the build-up of fear before the event was so great that I began to dread each Tuesday night as it approached, so I did not re-enrol for another term.

I investigated distance education in various subjects and this proved worthwhile. However, I couldn't bear to complete the course and not have the achievement of sitting for the examination. Knowing that fear would prevent me from doing so, I requested special permission and was able to complete the paper in my home, under supervision. The results were pleasing, so I pressed on. When examination time came the following year I really didn't feel justified in asking for special consideration a second time, and decided I would force myself to go and sit for the exam like all the other students.

Then, there were of course no mobile phones to provide contact but my husband took me there and promised faithfully that he would not leave the car, parked close by, so I could find him should I need to. Somehow I managed to complete the paper, and I even passed the exam, but I remember feeling that I was putting myself to an extreme test. Surely it was bad enough to be afraid to leave my home, without making myself go through the misery of an examination room as well. Anyway, I survived it — somehow we always do — and I believe it is worthwhile to keep trying and never give in, although now I know there are easier ways of going about it.

The year after that, I attempted another subject by correspondence, but because it was more complex, and really required tutorials and discussion with other students, my progress was halted — because I just couldn't make that kind of commitment. For the person with such high levels of anxiety, nothing in life is simple.

How difficult it is to make an appointment at the hairdresser's or to face the prospect of the walk to kindergarten! To buy those new tiny jeans, call at the library, share coffee with a friend or pick up take-away at the end of the day!

A visit to the hairdresser should be a soothing and pleasant experience. To a woman in a state of fear, a visit to the hairdresser is nothing short of an endurance test. First she has to go through the misery of actually keeping the appointment; having arrived there is sure to be a tedious wait to challenge the tension level if the salon is busy. Then will follow the powerful trapped feelings as the routine unfolds during which, rather than enjoying the opportunity to relax and be pampered, the anxious woman's sense of urgency almost pushes her to rush from the salon in a state of disrepair. That of course, will never happen; somehow we steel ourselves and see it all through, possibly promising that we will never go through this again. So this event becomes another unpleasant memory to add to those before it.

The same feelings arise – even in retail therapy! It is virtually impossible for an agoraphobic person to enter a fitting room without experiencing intense anxiety – with the result that garments are purchased and never worn. Under pressure, the person in fear of panic will very likely complete any transaction just to escape and dash home to 'safety'.

Restaurants and theatres hold their own type of apprehension. A preference to be seated near the door or on an aisle where the exit can be easily reached cannot always be arranged. While trying to appear to be enjoying ourselves, we have a continuous monitor on our reactions, thinking: 'However will I cope if those feelings of panic strike now?' Of course we rarely find out, because at the first appearance of any symptoms we manage either to leave discreetly at some appropriate moment, or to fight it through anyway, thereby saving face. But life is not being fully lived; the occasion has lost its sparkle. And because of the inhibiting fear, the pleasure of the most minor moments in life is lost through lack of spontaneity.

Yet people also have their pride; a natural sense of dignity and self-worth prevents their absolute surrender to fear. Should something be demanded where all excuses have failed and we cannot avoid leaving the house without losing face in the sight of others, somehow we will achieve it.

Gwen, who had been agoraphobic for over thirty years, recalled this story. A neighbour whom she greatly admired was giving a rather important dinner party, and during the evening suddenly realised she had forgotten to buy cream for the dessert. She phoned Gwen (not knowing of her anxiety) asking her to do her the favour of buying some cream to save her party. Gwen had no choice but to agree. Gwen said:

> I certainly didn't want her to know that I was afraid to go to the shop, and I wanted to help her anyway. But I was terrified that I would fail and be overwhelmed by panic in doing so … and although I was shaking with fear every step of the way and to me it was a tremendous ordeal, my friend got her cream!

After an incident such as that (which really can be a huge mission for a person with agoraphobia) the individual will hope that it will mark the beginning of the end of fear, and will feel certain that having forced him/herself through fear, freedom will result. But no! A new day will dawn and all the anxious feelings will be ready and waiting as companions to whatever has to be done, because, through tension, fear is still the master.

This problem does not respond to logic either. We cannot say to ourselves with success: 'All right, sometimes I experience these dreadful symptoms that I don't understand. But that's my problem and I'll just have to learn to live with it.' The sickening symptoms persist although we are doing our best, and they affect us and those around us constantly.

Although during those years I joined committees and attended meetings under great strain, among my greatest dreads were those very meetings, or church services or any organised occasion where I felt confined. How often does the well-meaning clergyman or chairperson inadvertently cause misery to 'those people standing at the back — there's plenty of room for you to be comfortable in the front row!' If only such people understood! The back row is preferred, seated right on the aisle. I don't think I ever did leave any such occasion because of panic, but the amount of nervous tension and energy that it took exhausts me, now, to think about it.

The years rolled on. Children were born, people died, there were weddings and christenings and funerals. Christmases and birthdays came and went, we visited old friends, made new ones, took holidays to various places and entertained at home. And during that time our family number increased to five with the birth of another lovely daughter. We settled the older two at school, encouraged them in all their new interests, attended business functions, participated in Boy Scout's barbecues and took part in those many other diversions that come with being a parent, along with the fun and duties involved. Life changed and developed all the time and I was right in it, but not without a good deal of fear and tension.

Moving house again, we began another renovation. I vaguely hoped that a different house would dispel my fear, but of course it didn't — how could it when the fear was within me? I was busy, and renovating is a creative hobby to say the least, but I lived for years with wallpaper that I detested because it was chosen in haste and under pressure while desiring escape from confinement in the shop.

Because my children did not know of my fear, and because I always wanted to do for them everything I could to the best of my ability, I constantly forced myself to be involved in everything that affected them. The needs of young children are not easily forecast, and are more immediate and therefore of extra concern. There is always the thought in the back of your mind that illness or accident will occur and you will have to face taking the child to hospital in an emergency. You also know, deep down, that if you have to do it, you will, and very ably. But you go on dreading that it might happen and hoping like mad that it won't. Fortunately for me there was only one such emergency, and a fairly minor one, and of course I dealt with it.

Another woman with the same fear recalled how only once in many years the school phoned to tell her that one of her children was ill. She was saved from having to leave her home in that small emergency by her partner who happened to come home for something forgotten and was able to collect the child on her behalf. But I believe that had he not been available, she would have found the courage to rise to the occasion.

That is not to say that the fear is inconsistent; it is always there and we suffer much in doing these things, but we can force ourselves past it when something of this nature occurs or somebody needs us. The anxious person seeking freedom is always striving and will rarely give up, but because he or she is going about it the wrong way, it is all very hard work.

In those years, whenever necessary I took the children to the dentist or to the doctor, or to school interviews or any other event which involved their well-being. I became astute at arranging appointments so that we were either first or last to be attended to. Detailed organisation would to some degree, reduce the fear of having to *wait* too long for the practitioner.

In those years I tried as often as possible to make myself participate in all the duties that particularly involved mothers and their children. I remember well when, for a time, I forced myself to help with voluntary assistance in a classroom. In retrospect I probably should have had more sense than to torture myself unnecessarily for tasks like those were carried out more from a sense of resolve than from duty or personal enjoyment. Terrified that I would be stricken somehow by the recurring symptoms I worried about all the children in my care.

I can look back now and say: 'Why worry? Let's live in the 'now" for life is precarious enough anyway and disaster — real disaster — can strike at any time, yet we don't dwell upon it.' But in those years, the fear which I couldn't see or touch or run from haunted me, and the part I played in any situation of responsibility was of great consequence to me. By the way, focus on the "now" when the "now" is primarily anxiety symptoms is not a welcome recommendation either!

Should the observer think in reading this that anxious people are merely procrastinators totally preoccupied with their own well-being, let me hasten to correct this impression. Often it is with thought of others that fear is foremost in our minds; in particular of course, the young, the elderly, or indeed anyone relying upon our presence.

At the same time, we don't want that person who is relying upon us to sense our insecurity, so we tense up and fight it through. How could I, when in my thirties, 163 cm tall, of proportionate weight and looking extremely healthy, have said to a trainee teacher at the nearby kindergarten (who only looked like a child herself): 'Don't leave me alone and responsible for these little children; I might faint.' Absolutely ridiculous! Yet the fear still hovered.

The fact that I continually forced myself to do these things at least gave me some extra feeling of accomplishment in life, but it was all very difficult and although I fought hard, I was still going about it the wrong way. All these achievements were within that one-kilometre radius of home, and if anything was organised at a venue other than those local ones, unless it was something to which my husband could also go, I would decline. And many times I did just that, when fear won the battle over reason. Often I would have to defer an appointment or ask my husband to fulfil whatever was in hand in my place, or have him accompany me.

One of the most displeasing aspects of these conditions is that lack of personal freedom. We cannot, on impulse, take the dog for a walk, risk a queue at the bank, or fly a kite in the park with the children. Life must be planned and actions are preceded by the words 'but' or 'if'. As for the prospect of extensive travel – that is largely unthinkable! But the simple things hurt the most – like the inability to comfortably attend to local shopping. By arranging deliveries, I had perfected the technique of never running out of necessities. (Later, with spontaneity restored, I seemed to be always running out of everything!) However, just occasionally, something would be required that could only be found at the supermarket. This becomes a place of immense apprehension. Understandably so, with jostling people, bright lights and noise, dazzling products to confuse, loud background music or miked voices arresting attention, slow queues at the checkouts; and once inside, you are usually a long way from the exit! No wonder people who are tense and anxious commonly detest the modern supermarket, food hall or shopping complex. And no wonder many a store manager finds the odd can of pet food in the refrigerator or breakfast cereal with the soap powder or even an occasional fully-loaded shopping trolley completely abandoned — some poor shopper, overcome by panic, has fled the store. So in those years, when something was needed, we either had to manage without it until the next delivery, or my husband would collect a few items, or the older children would go to the small store nearby.

The highly anxious, tense, agoraphobic person will dread a visit to the dentist. It is difficult enough having to leave the house, but then there is the possibility of having to pass a long time in the waiting room. When finally admitted to the surgery, then comes the feeling of being 'trapped' in the dental chair. Comedians can have a field day with dental procedures; the dark glasses, many objects in and around the mouth, no easy exit past a tray of implements and a vacuum cleaning device at the ready. Longing for escape but too afraid to try, the palms sweat and tension rises more as the observant dentist attempts to distract the patient in what eventuates in a one-way conversation. In those days, I too, had a great aversion to dental appointments. I had no fear of dental work – but was preoccupied with the terror of feeling so trapped – with the possibility of panic occurring.

I understand now the significance of the dentist's words to the patient. But I wonder how many dentists, and certainly how many patients, really realise the importance of what is being said? Many such situations can be improved by the patient's understanding of what it means to relax. The feeling of being unable to endure an event such as that with ease is caused by the tension used to fight the symptoms — the vicious circle again — and is quite a common problem.

It is easy to look back with experience and see how one thing complicated another. But none of this was clear to me then; trapped as I was by feelings that amounted to a mystery. Had I understood then the patterns and reactions that built that mystery with the clarity of today, *agoraphobia* as such would most likely not have arisen.

However, it did – and with determination I finally accessed further professional help in the following manner. The time was approaching when my little boy was to start at a new school. I wondered how I was going to face the commitment of taking him there and collecting him again each day. The constant fear of being suddenly overwhelmed by the dreaded attack worried me more than ever. Despite continued enquiries, I still had no understanding as to why I continually met with the mysterious symptoms. There seemed to be no way of losing 'it' and no assurance that it would disappear of its own volition.

Worse than all that, my confidence was broken. I had never been an especially nervous or highly-strung person; in fact quite the contrary: I was the one on whom people tended to lean, and I greatly disliked this feeling of vulnerability. I was confused and unhappy; I couldn't find a solution, and I was beginning to think that I was destined to spend the rest of my life within the confines of my home.

Something had to be done. As any medical practitioner I had consulted to date had been unable to supply an answer to my riddle, I sought the advice of a Catholic priest. Also a psychologist and social worker, and somewhat ahead of his time, he had no doubt dealt with many, varied problems.

To see him I had to force myself to take a tram trip to his office. That day also marked my last excursion on public transport for many years. The symptoms were intense and the subsequent fear was very great on my way to keep the appointment. Yet when I related my story to him it sounded, to me, extremely trivial and unimportant. To my amazement, he showed understanding. Apart from my husband, with his continued and loving tolerance, this priest was the first person to whom I spoke about my fear who could at least comprehend my difficulty. To the embarrassment of both of us, I wept uncontrollably simply from the fact that somebody *listened*. He had not buried my problem under a pile of prescriptions!

He suggested that, as fear is an emotion, I should discuss the matter with a psychiatrist who, he said, 'would be more capable of helping you to fight it than I am'. I really believed that the symptoms which followed me around could only be caused by some obscure physical ailment. It seemed impossible to me that such persistent symptoms of illness could have an emotional basis. At that time, I only associated psychiatry with mental illness, so his suggestion was inclined to alarm me further still.

I believe now that psychology is probably the most significant aspect of medical knowledge, and that an informed understanding of human behaviour by general practitioners is of great importance. For it seems that most human ills, if not caused by, are certainly complicated by, our emotions, and anything we learn or any way we can better understand our response to living can only be beneficial to all. In this age, our science and technology have helped our progress in many significant ways, but it can be easy to forget that people are still people, with worries and needs, hopes and dreams.

All those years ago I wasn't so sure, but although confused by the priest's recommendation, I would have done anything to overcome my symptoms and fear of leaving the house, so I agreed. He gave me a letter of introduction to, as he put it, 'a wise old doctor whom I know quite well'. I arranged a taxi to take me home, which somehow I safely reached once more, clutching proverbially at another straw.

Later that week I visited the psychiatrist. He was long-retired, seeing a few patients at his home. He was very correct, very kind, very understanding and very, very old. Once more, the whole story was told.

'My dear,' he whispered in the velvet tones unique to gentlemen of that generation, 'the persistent and unpleasant feelings you are experiencing are most certainly symptoms of anxiety. You have been under stress and the symptoms of anxiety have increased and persisted. They will pass with time.'

He seemed to understand what was puzzling me, and I had no reason nor any choice other than to believe in what he told me. But there was still no satisfactory conclusion to the problem of my fear of leaving the house. The prospect of having to put up with those symptoms of anxiety for an indefinite length of time, until they chose to leave me, was not something that pleased me at all.

I had several discussions with the elderly psychiatrist over a few weeks, most of which were fruitful, if apparently a little irrelevant to the situation that bothered me. But, although I respected his knowledge, he seemed to be part of another era. I felt that he was too old, too out of touch with the world to which I belonged to really help me. So, tactfully, I trust, I disengaged myself from further appointments.

As we parted, he gave me some advice, the kind of advice that can only come from the mass of wisdom gained from longevity. He said, and I have never forgotten a word: 'Never let your children see you distressed in any way. Never try to run a perfect house; be firm, but let the children be free. They must experience the feel of earth on their hands and feet — and let them have lots of animals for pets. And, my dear, never try to change the course of destiny.'

At least my talks with that inspirational man had given me a little hope. I was not imagining my uneasiness; it was something real, and surely something could be done about it. With a fragment of renewed courage, I went back to my local doctor and said firmly: 'Please refer me to the best psychiatrist you know of. I need someone to show me the way out of this maze of fear.'

Chapter 5

SEARCHING FOR A CAUSE

 ✹

It may be for years, and it may be for ever,
Oh! Why art thou silent, thou voice of my heart?

Julia Crawford, C19th

The psychiatrist I was sent to was a sincere and gentle man with great patience. He showed understanding of my fear. Like those before him, but more convincingly, he assured me that my recurring symptoms were not those of any latent physical ailment, reaffirming that they were caused by high anxiety. He explained that everyone's level of anxiety increases under stress, and we discussed to some extent the stresses I had encountered before that fateful day in the shopping centre. He suggested that the reason for my elevated anxiety was due either to a suppressed or long-forgotten childhood experience that had caused me alarm, or an unresolved conflict from my past of which I had been unconsciously reminded while under stress. He said that the symptoms which bothered me would disappear when such a conflict was discovered and freely discussed. To achieve this, he recommended psychoanalysis. In the meantime he prescribed medication, updating the Amytal to the then more popular Valium, which I could take as needed to lessen the symptoms and make life easier.

To further reassure me, he also stated that I was an intelligent, articulate and attractive woman with a strong and stable personality and good qualities to contribute to life. I found this summing-up reassuring and felt a little less embarrassed about my fear. My ever-dwindling confidence and somewhat crushed ego was therefore slightly revitalised. On the strength of this summarisation, the doctor indicated that there seemed to be no reason why I should not overcome my fear with little delay.

I was grateful for his reassurance and, as he seemed confident of success, I was willing to co-operate with analysis in order to be free again. If something in my life was revealed that was causing me anxiety, the symptoms would then disappear and obviously so would my fear of leaving the safety of home. However, the idea didn't make a great deal of sense to me. My life held no unpleasant memories and had been generally safe and happy; I was not weighed with any major disturbance from the past. So what kind of quest were we undertaking?

Fear of leaving the house (the word 'agoraphobia' had still not been identified) for fear of further 'attacks' (the fact that those attacks were panic was not clearly stated either) was my difficulty. It seemed now to be a chicken-and-egg situation; was I afraid to leave the house because I was experiencing anxiety from something in my past? Or was I experiencing anxiety simply because I was afraid to leave the house? I seemed to be getting into deep water. But how else to overcome my fear?

Recollecting all the stressful events in the first months of my marriage made it clear to me that certainly stress had increased my level of anxiety and must obviously have contributed to that initial attack.

Over subsequent years' discussion with others, it is obvious that the degree of stress necessary to set up the chain reaction of panic varies greatly with the individual. The aftermath of an operation, the birth of a child, a death in the family, relationship issues or the loss of a job are recalled by many as the incidents which preceded their anxiety condition. Some have included illness or workplace pressure and others describe an amalgam of stressors comprised of change, disruptions and shocks over a period of time. Here are some stories:

Jane, a single girl, was in a car accident. Although she was not severely injured, she was deeply upset by the injuries sustained by another person. Shortly after the accident she became chronically ill, and after many months her illness was finally diagnosed as a thyroid condition and she was operated on. She had become extremely worried while awaiting the diagnosis and during the preceding months of illness, and therefore did not make a good recovery after the operation. She continued to feel unwell after returning to work, and experienced anxiety symptoms and panic at work. She finally gave up her job. This, she claims, was her big mistake, for once she was not pressed to leave for work each day, she began to find it difficult to leave the house at all, and soon developed agoraphobia.

When I first met Judith, a youthful married woman with three adult children, she had been agoraphobic for twenty years. She was not totally confined to home and held a responsible position, but was unable to venture far from her own locality without her husband close at hand. Her fear developed after the birth of her first child, as a result of the stress of what she describes as 'the over-whelming responsibility of motherhood'. It became increasingly difficult for her to leave her home, as she continually experienced panic when out of the house, and she spent many years as a prisoner of fear when her family was younger.

Lynne's agoraphobia began after a severe panic attack in the local butcher's shop. She was a nurse in the children's wing of a major hospital. She recalled that she took her responsibilities very seriously, and was under considerable stress as she became emotionally involved with the young patients.

Rod was a Navy man who had worked for many years out of doors. Leaving that role, he then joined an airline company, attaining a senior position of responsibility which involved long hours and shift work. Workplace stress apparently led to panic attacks and he believed that working indoors was the cause of his anxiety. He left that position hoping that his symptoms would ease once he was out in the open again. Of course, that was not the solution, and he subsequently lost three further positions due to agoraphobia, thus ending his professional life.

Helen, an agoraphobic for twenty-six years, became so after a panic attack combined with a severe migraine headache while out shopping with her young baby. The stress which preceded the attack began with blood pressure problems during her pregnancy, and the fact that when the baby was born her husband became ill with a viral infection and was not permitted to visit her or the baby for two weeks. She added: 'Then I had no sleep for six weeks, as the baby did not stop crying. I was exhausted.'

Eighteen-year-old Michael developed agoraphobia in Year 11 at high school. When he was eleven, due to failing eyesight, he was prescribed glasses, but was too shy to wear them to school, a stressful situation at that age. His poor vision prevented him from reading the board clearly and he became more and more anxious and panicky that he wouldn't get a seat in the front row. Consequently his anxiety increased with the years, until he found himself experiencing panic out in the street and began to stay home more and more after leaving school.

Maureen was agoraphobic for eight years following panic while suffering severe depression. For eleven years preceding that depression, she was under stress, nursing her sick mother, and also, for part of that time, a close friend who was terminally ill. Both died within a very short time of each other and Maureen felt their loss with devastation and loneliness.

When I met Neville, a bachelor, he had suffered agoraphobia for nearly twenty years. On a regular medical check in his twenties he was told, incorrectly as it happened, that he had high blood pressure. This was cause for worry, especially when soon afterwards the father of a friend died suddenly of a stroke. Then Neville's mother died. When anxiety symptoms began to occur he worried that these were symptoms relating to his blood pressure. Soon after, his sister unexpectedly died and around the same time, he broke off a relationship. A few months later by way of distraction he decided to 'have a good night out' and play golf the next day. It was during the game that he experienced severe panic and life has been complicated for him since then by agoraphobia.

All these people exhibited tension, a response that has been with them for years. The stress that preceded their lasting problem of agoraphobia had been coped with up to the 'elastic limit' of each person, and they had fought hard with tension as their anxiety level increased. Interestingly, most spent many years fighting without knowing that what they were fighting was panic. I had done likewise, and fear had intruded into my life. It seemed that the only solution to my problem was to commence psychoanalysis in the hope that life revelation would bring cure and free me from bondage.

The psychiatrist took my fear seriously and was always kind and, above all, compassionate. He had still put no name to the panic attack and referred to what I feared as 'anxious feelings'. So what I actually dreaded was still, in itself, a mystery to me, which no doubt increased my fear of fear. More importantly, then, I still did not realise or understand the fact that I, too, was a slave to tension.

Obviously, being afraid to leave home meant that keeping regular appointments for psychoanalysis was very difficult. For therapy to have any chance of success, regular appointments were essential. But to achieve this, I had to leave the house and go to the doctor's rooms. If I chose not to go, I felt I was denying myself the only hope of overcoming the symptoms and, consequently, my fear. And yet keeping the appointments was overwhelmingly difficult.

This went on for many months. The main benefit of analysis to date was the fact that having to keep the appointments at least forced me out of the house on those occasions, and the psychiatrist was able to provide some degree of the reassurance necessary to me.

My husband convinced me that I should have a car again, and as being without one had not fixed anything, I agreed. The car soon became a crutch, a form of security, and in it I could travel more easily that one kilometre distance. Even though I began to accept that the recurring symptoms were those of anxiety, their power over me filled me with terror. Nevertheless I was more fortunate than those who cannot face anything past their front door.

In therapy, sometimes it occurred to me that the psychiatrist himself did not really comprehend the utter misery I was experiencing, for each time he spoke the simple phrase 'come back in two weeks', that very suggestion in itself would send a knife-like shock of fear throughout me. Yet I would bravely agree. So I struggled on, dreading the appointments, changing them often, feeling guilty for doing so, and all the while never feeling one bit of improvement. But there was apparently no alternative.

I would wake on the morning of the appointment in an immensely fearful state at the thought of having to leave the house and face a trip to the *city*. If it was one of the days when my husband was not available to take me to the appointment, I knew that I would either have to go alone, or not go at all. I would begin the day by trying to decide whether I would risk driving my own car, take a taxi or travel by public transport.

Public transport was definitely still out. To have taken a bus, I would first have had to walk to the bus-stop and *wait*. The awful symptoms would certainly arise during that time, and if they didn't then, they surely would as soon as I had stepped on board as that trapped, claustrophobic, out of control feeling flooded reality. There would then most likely have been further panic, grappling with a decision: to remain there and complete the journey or the awful alternative of disembarking in terror and finding oneself in some unfamiliar and equally alarming area, a long way from home. I had previously managed to avoid that circumstance but the idea itself was so distressing that I could not contemplate this option. Of course, had I done so and remained on the bus, and assuming I could find my way safely to my destination, I still had to get home again. So as far as I was concerned, public transport was not a remote consideration.

To take a taxi every time I had an appointment was usually only one-way security, too. I always felt that while I would get to my destination without the degree of anxiety that would be associated with public transport, I had the added worry of not knowing whether or not a taxi would be readily available to take me home again — and getting back home, to the agoraphobic, is the most important part of any outing. So there arose a secondary problem, as I didn't want to risk being stranded in the city.

One woman in that predicament told me how she became overwhelmed by panic and rushed up to a policeman for help. She must have chosen an understanding policeman, for he was able to assure her while securing a taxi for her safe return home. The agoraphobic needs this security, this feeling of being prevented from 'that attack', so very much that although to some people taking taxis everywhere may seem extravagant, the agoraphobic would pay any price to avoid suffering what he or she fears. Over the years I did take many taxis, and I found this means of transport provided a level of comfort necessary under such conditions.

My third choice was to drive my own car. That was still about the most difficult thing I could face. Short distances close to home – not too bad. But a casual drive into the city – just not on. Writing this I am reminded again, of the terrifying unreality of these situations where all one's usual senses seem to have run amok and all judgment becomes clouded. Distances appear visibly stretched to infinity as hypnotically, metres appear to lengthen into kilometres and a sense of suffocation and overwhelm is very strong. The traffic takes on greater noise, congestion and confusion. Crowds feel oppressive and finding somewhere to park satisfactorily generates feelings of being 'lost'. Central car-parks are ominous and even the prospect of leaving the car out of the CBD to walk the distance raises extremes of fear.

After considering all three options for getting to the appointment, I would frequently be overpowered by the very thought of having to go through with this, and plead with my husband to alter his programme for the day and accompany me. Then I would be wracked with guilt, while frustration and anger at my encumbrance converted to tears.

Having brought all those worries upon myself, I would then be unable to eat a thing; yet I would fear that if I didn't eat something I might feel weak, which might then precipitate the dreaded attack. And because of the fear of feeling faint and weak, I would then agonise over what to wear. Anxiety generates body heat and being too warmly clad can create yet another fear of disaster! Such worry — and what a dilemma.

Then there would be a minder to organise for the children, and I would be worried about leaving them, always afraid deep down that those symptoms would deal their final blow while I was away from home.

After I'd done all this worrying in anticipation of fear, which now seems so futile, I would have to make the decision as to whether or not I could actually keep the appointment that day! I have always been a person with a strict sense of responsibility, and dislike cancelling or changing things. But with all the preliminary worry about going out of the house I would, by now, be feeling decidedly 'wrung out'. The temptation to phone and say that I couldn't keep the appointment was very great, and this would also eliminate immediately all the things I had just spent ages worrying about. But, no treatment, no freedom — or so it seemed. What turmoil. And what a waste of energy. And how aware I was of the irrationality surrounding my entrapment, even then.

Eventually I would find myself on the way to the psychiatrist's rooms, with much apprehension – my constant travelling companion. I would then invariably have to wait to see the doctor for anything up to an hour. Waiting, waiting… One seems to be in such a state of urgency, only wanting to get home to safety again, so that even the thought of having to wait will stir up symptoms. This is, of course, caused by the continuing tension which makes endurance impossible. But we do not realise this, and go on fighting our reactions, worsening our situation by the minute.

I would try to distract myself by browsing through a magazine, but inevitably there would be some article in it which would not help. Every time a worried person picks up a paper there seems to be some article on physical disease describing symptoms to match those being experienced. I sometimes used to think, if I was feeling light-hearted, that this was a service from the media to the medical profession – to give the doctor a few good reactions to work on! Of course, had I but known endurance of the waiting room itself could have been a valuable starting point in consultation when my turn to see him eventually arrived.

I have heard people who have experienced psychoanalysis complain that they have spent every session mercilessly discussing the themes of Freudian sexuality. Thankfully this doctor did not relentlessly pursue themes of that nature; if he had, I think I would have felt that I had succumbed to a living cliché. However, that was not the path he chose to take. We examined, primarily, my childhood and later years, people who affected my life and the meaning of dreams. It seemed to be important to analysis to relate current situations which produced anxiety symptoms, to any similar experiences of my childhood. But as my mounting sensations of anxiety seemed to occur at any time and in any situation outside the home, this was almost an impossibility. Each visit was the same, and we were not making positive progress. I would make another appointment and go home, only a little more easily than I had come, to resume my limited life once more until the next appointment.

And still I did not understand that the attack which I lived in fear of was *panic*, the natural response to fear. Over and above the problem of being constantly afraid to leave the house, there was something else that concerned me; and it was something which I knew I didn't understand.

Although reassured by the doctor to a certain degree, possessing those symptoms worried me. I viewed my fear as a problem exclusive to myself, as though I had suddenly sprouted wings or a spare pair of hands. I felt that experiencing anxiety in this way was an indication of weakness or failure, and I felt burdened by something I couldn't dispense with. In my ignorance I did not understand then that anxiety is part of life. It may be reassuring to many at this point to reiterate that there are almost no fears, thoughts or feelings that are not experienced by others. There is no need to feel alone; but there is need to understand. Time passed, and after a number of visits the psychiatrist came to the conclusion that my anxiety was caused primarily by suppressed anger. Far later in my story I came to accept this possibility, along with many other 'conditioning' factors, as contributing to the big anxiety-producing picture. But at that time, any fragment of self-awareness that could have been helpful was masked by the dominance of my very invasive state of tension. I was constantly tense, fighting from within, in the misguided belief that by holding every -thing together, so to speak, I was 'in control'.

However, at one particular consultation, this conclusion was re-it-erated quite emphatically: 'You're very angry, Pauline. Your anxiety is caused by so many angry feelings — feelings that you haven't expressed.'

'Nonsense,' said I. 'I'm never angry, and I certainly don't feel angry right now.' I remember he laughed — very kindly.

He went on. 'You're far too "nice". You're making life extremely dif-ficult for yourself by continually being so obliging.'

I had no idea what he was talking about. I just simply lived; the only way I knew how. And I wanted to be free of fear to participate in life as I had once known it.

I thought about this conversation for a few days. It occurred to me that perhaps I was not contributing enough to psychoanalysis and that I should be making a more concerted effort to alter certain aspects of my personality, to release the anger the doctor spoke of, and thereby hasten a remedy for my fear.

The most obvious person to practise on was my husband. I tried very hard to be aggressive, but aggression is just not my style and this only amused him. I tried to be more assertive, but it only irritated him, as it was a false display of assertion. I tried to find an opportunity when he would really make me very angry and I could tell him so. No such op-portunity presented itself to my awareness.

Then I remembered that an angry woman is more than capable of serving the evening meal to her partner on a speeding plate, delivered somewhere between nose and knees when the unfortunate male has saun-tered in late and with no valid reason to excuse him. Why couldn't I react like that? I wasn't prepared to sacrifice any lengthily prepared dinner for such an exercise, but the next time my husband forgot the time without justification, I threw a dish of summer-soft butter. Of course, one cannot pre-meditate angry reactions, or any emotional reaction for that matter, and naturally the butter missed its target. He just stood there laughing good-naturedly as my plan of self-help went somewhat awry. I spent an hour cleaning a rather greasy kitchen.

'Did you feel any better for having done that?' asked the psychiatrist on my next visit.

Did I feel any better? Of course I didn't feel any better — I had had to clean it all up. And I was still terrified to walk out the front door.

He tried to console me by praising my sense of humour.

Chapter 6

ON FRIENDSHIP

ꙮ

A friend is someone who knows everything
about us and still accepts us.

St Augustine

One afternoon as I was sitting dejectedly in my garden trying to read a book, and wishing I was taking my family somewhere interesting for all of us, I was called to the side fence by my friend and neighbour. She attracted my attention by waving an unopened bottle of sherry. At that time she had four little children and was leading a busy and stressful life herself, and she obviously understood that all was not entirely well with me. I think she probably assumed that I, like so many women can be, was overwhelmed by the duties and responsibilities of those busy years of mothering. We have since recalled this incident with amusement and it has stayed in my memory because of her insight at that time. She practically forced the bottle of sherry upon me, saying; 'I don't drink at all, but I'm sure you'll cope better if you have some of this.' I took it from her only because I was touched by her concern, and her insistence was great. Actually, I don't like sherry much, which was probably fortunate, or I may have taken her advice too literally, demolished the entire bottle and set myself upon a far worse course than that which I was already following.

But despite the fact that she had reached out with the hand of friendship, I could not bring myself to tell her that fear was disturbing my life. I was greatly ashamed of my fear and I was 'scared' to admit to it. Friends who later learned of that difficulty have expressed amazement: 'I never would have guessed, you certainly concealed it well.' This is so. Most who endure anxiety and agoraphobia do conceal the problem very well, and no-one but the closest person to us will ever catch a glimpse of the misery and distress suffered in private as one is confronted with having to leave the house.

As already noted, when submerged by fear, I believed that I was alone with the problem and I carried a self-inflicted stigma because of this. Many others do likewise. Even today, with far greater public consciousness of anxiety disorders, people of all ages and either gender are still reluctant to share their fear openly — out of a sense of shame. So generally, the victim of fear will endeavour to hide their difficulty from all but the chosen confidant and continue to carry the problem primarily on his or her own shoulders. And yet if communication and discussion with trusted friends and relatives could relieve some part of the anxiety, it must be useful to attempt this.

Anxious people are sensitive. In their sensitivity (a gift of their natural temperament), they invariably worry that their fear, while already ruining the normality of their life, if admitted to, will adversely affect their reputation too. Then the anxious person falls prey to imagining what might happen, should they share their story. These speculations, in my opinion, identify a significant element of the anxiety condition: the fear of rejection. The shame and humiliation associated with rejection can also invent a major stumbling block in the individual's progress to freedom.

Because enduring fear fractures confidence and self-esteem, those burdened become adept at protecting themselves from any hurt whatsoever. This is understandable of course, as part of one's need for self-preservation. However, in preserving oneself from rejection, shame, hurt or humiliation, the need to defend oneself is further heightened. Anxiety, at many levels, remains high and substantial energy — and notable tension — is required to maintain this natural, if exaggerated, need.

So even in the matter of friendships, which ought be healing, the fear-filled person is juggling various facets of anxiety. And yet, a problem shared certainly *is* a problem halved. The sharing of the story *can* help eliminate a portion of that anxiety.

Most people, anxious or otherwise, tread cautiously around the area of personal disclosure. The agoraphobic person treads *very* cautiously. However, if such a person can have the courage to make the first move, he or she can find new support and may indirectly help someone else as well. But there is risk involved, which then raises a choice: should this person confide in their friends and find loving support? Or, if this step is taken, will tenuous threads of confidence be torn apart should the person so trusted respond with some form of rejection?

It is not easy, I know, for the person with agoraphobia to discuss the problem freely. It seems such a foolish thing for an adult person to be afraid of leaving their own home, particularly when there are so many specific and serious troubles in the world to claim more importance. This person is faced with a difficult decision, for, having spoken, the choice of confidant may have been a poor one, and the risk of regret, alongside the possibility of benefit, is very great. And it is true that there are people who are insensitive or uncaring of others' needs.

In discussing this dilemma with a friend, we talked about the pros and cons of whether people can and should assist one another through emotional difficulties. This was a delicate conversation, for the man I was speaking with was, at the time, caring for his wife who was dying of cancer. I was impressed by one particular comment though, when he observed that it seems to be much easier to help others emotionally when you are in the midst of emotional suffering yourself. One person's suffering seems to make other sufferings acceptable. Therefore, in choosing a new confidant, it may be useful to bear in mind that people of similar sensitivity, and people who have some life experience in personal pain, are more likely to respond in kind.

The person in fear is also cautious around the family. The first time my children knew that I had experienced a fear of this nature was in the early stages of planning this book. I took aside my then teenage son and daughter on separate occasions and explained to them what I had in mind. It came to me as a pleasant surprise when each, independently, gave me great encouragement. With enthusiasm, both said, in their own way: 'Yes, you must write it; it's very important that people understand these things.'

I was greatly relieved by their loving reassurance and friendship. I had expected them to have reacted with frivolity or embarrassment at my story. Since then, I have observed the reactions of other young people to the subject, and to similar matters concerning human emotion. The result has been very much the same.

From some current educational approaches, today's youth has the opportunity to grasp the skills of empathy and communication far more so than former generations. I know at their age I would not have been so appreciative of emotional need and perhaps not so compassionate. While people can be insensitive to others' pain, this may be due to an insular upbringing where, protected like porcelain in a glass box from many of the truths of life, they find it difficult to relate to matters to which they have not been exposed. But youth today see it all and while there can also be a downside to that exposure, if attempting to share deep feelings one is likely to be reasonably safe in the hands of the upcoming generation.

However, during my years of fear, I refrained from telling my kids. I think when children are very young, that decision is a wise one. It was my feeling then that if a mother admitted fear to her children, they might feel insecure also. I could not allow that to happen. I also worried that, if the children knew, they might mention it to other children, or worse still, in the hearing of other parents. Once again, here was the risk of people knowing my shame.

But keeping such fear from other people is quite a strain, for there are so many situations to be negotiated. It may seem strange to the reader who has not experienced a phobic reaction that a mother can keep this fear from her children for many years. But the anxious person becomes very adept at 'keeping a stiff upper lip', emanating ease and enjoyment no matter what is felt within, and fabricating that endless repertoire of excuses as to why he or she cannot do this or that. This is not deliberate deception. It is a role, well played by conscientious people, to avoid panic and to save face. But oh, how this keeps the fire of fear smouldering!

These days, when I speak openly to others about having experienceed agoraphobia, almost every person to whom I speak knows of someone else who is similarly hiding that fear. And certainly everyone with whom this fear is discussed knows of some type of fear, either through their personal experience or that of another.

An interesting question now arises. In my case, is the reaction of the people to whom I have spoken only positive and enthusiastic because I have already overcome the problem? And would people react in the same way if I was saying that I was still agoraphobic? The answer can only be speculative. Unfortunately, greater glory is always handed out to those who can say they have overcome a difficulty. And it seems to be a trait of human nature to be critical of those in the midst of difficulties, even while at the same time possibly trying to help. Personally, I have not met with a rejection: perplexity sometimes, but never a rebuff or an outright rejection. Perhaps this could be because, in overcoming fear, people's reactions do not concern me as they might have done before.

In the case of others, a crystal ball could be handy to advise on whom to choose to confide in and whom to avoid telling. As one woman put it: 'I've had no success in telling people about agoraphobia. I usually get a blank stare while the person tries to decide whether to back me in the last race or back off in case I'm contagious!'

Then she added: 'Some may say, "What a shame. Oh, but that's nothing, you just have to forget that and make yourself get over it."' Hardly a very insightful reply. Perhaps she has just been unlucky, but these responses do tend to make the sufferer want to forget the idea of opening up to others.

After many years of fear, I did eventually confide in several friends, and their reactions were always favourable and helpful. My first experience of sharing this was when I tentatively spoke of my fear to a close woman friend. I had hardly finished speaking when she, with the same sense of relief, told me that she also suffered quite similarly. A professional woman, she worked full time and always found that the commitment of her work helped her cope with her fear. However, driving to and from the office was a particular problem to her. She dealt with it in a very pragmatic manner and always travelled by the same route where she had to pass several pharmacies. If the panic feeling began to occur, as a matter of routine she would immediately park the car, go to the pharmacist and ask for something to calm her. After she had regained her composure, she was then able to continue her journey

On the other hand, Marie, a single woman of middle age whose agoraphobic history covered more than twelve years, has only told her older sister of the problem. From Marie's description, her sister is overbearing and Marie has allowed herself to be literally 'pushed around' as her sister challenges her to action – not helpful at all. Tension and embarrassment may cause people to fumble, drop things, forget things and so on and when Marie becomes flooded by panic this is confirmation to her that she is simply a nervous wreck, incapable of coping with anything, while her sister's status rises in this sibling contest. No wonder Marie is anxious! She is in trepidation at the prospect of her sister's visits – yet cannot bring herself to confide in anyone else for support.

A good example of friendship strengthened by the capacity to understand is that of Jenny, an agoraphobia sufferer of eleven years. A bubbly woman in her thirties with a good sense of humour, Jenny told this story. The friend in whom she had confided wanted to buy a garment for a special occasion and asked Jenny to accompany her. Jenny was not too keen on department stores, especially when evening wear was on the eighth floor! However, she agreed to go with her friend, but stressed the point that she could only go as long as her friend didn't leave her side. Her friend was sympathetic and seemed to understand Jenny's need. At the same time she herself was feeling on top of the world at the prospect of her purchase, and it wasn't too long before she was in the fitting room and Jenny was left alone.

Jenny recalled: 'I couldn't see her anywhere; she had absolutely disappeared and I was on my own, in an unfamiliar and enormous store, crowded by people and garments and eight floors up in the elevator.' She was able to laugh about it later.

'As panic began to mount, I found a post and hung on to that for support, thinking: someone will find me eventually, even if it's not until the store closes.'

When her friend swept out of the fitting room, looking a million dollars in her new outfit, she did find Jenny, still clutching the post. She was shocked and surprised that in her own light-heartedness she had over-looked the intensity of Jenny's need not to be left. She amended her innocent mistake by linking her arm through Jenny's and promising not to let go until they were safely back at street level. Undoubtedly a greater sense of companionship was reached through that incident, providing support for Jenny in dealing with fear.

Here is another slant on the various reactions of different people whom agoraphobia sufferers have confided in. A woman who had suffered with that condition for 17 years eventually told her two daughters who were, by then, young adults. Of course they accepted it very readily, offering encouragement and any kind of help their mother might require. The older girl, who was by that time living away from home, made a special arrangement whereby her mother could always contact her should she feel the need to. The younger daughter was very easily able to understand her mother's fear, as she herself had a great fear of spiders, so they were able to discuss fear openly and objectively together. When these girls were asked by their mother whether, as little children, they had ever wondered why they were never taken out by their mother alone, they said that the thought had never occurred to them. They simply remembered always going everywhere together, as a family. So, for all her effort in keeping her difficulty from her family, the mother was the only one who had endured any deprivation; no-one else had missed out on anything because of her agoraphobia, and now that the family knew, they couldn't do enough to help.

In contrast, Irene, when she finally told her young adult daughters that she was agoraphobic, found that although the girls readily paid lip-service to her problem and gave the appearance of understanding, in the next breath they would say: 'Would you pick up a few things at the sale for me today please, Mum, they'll be closed before I get home'. And 'Mum, perhaps your agoraphobia would go if you slowed down a bit and rested more!'

So Irene, who found it difficult to go to the market for the week's food supply, would endeavour to force herself across the road to the store with the sale. Perhaps she over-indulged her children by giving too much of herself, but this is a small example of how, ironically, people can force themselves to achieve what is usually impossible, though doing so will be immensely distressful.

But there can be unfortunate negative reactions to the sharing of confidence. Cheryl, who had a particular fear of being out at night, confided in a supposedly close friend. Her friend, possibly in a misguided attempt to help, invited Cheryl to spend the day with her, promising to drive her home afterwards. When the time came to leave, Cheryl's friend absolutely refused to drive her home, saying that she was making a fuss about nothing and she must find her own way home like any other sensible adult person. That 'sensible adult person' was quickly reduced to a fearful and tearful state as she was left to her own now weakened resources.

Cheryl said: 'I've never spoken to that person again. She used to be a close friend, but her lack of compassion hurt me so greatly that I can never really forgive her.'

Possibly even worse than total misunderstanding can be the absurdity of misinterpretation. Kath, an agoraphobic for a number of years, was a sweet-natured person, living alone and therefore rather isolated in fear. Eventually she summoned sufficient courage to divulge her secret to a neighbour. That was a huge step for Kath, and that neighbour could have been of tremendous support to her. But in this case it was not to be. Kath's biggest dread was of being in large stores and alone among crowds of people. The prospect of a visit to the local supermarket to buy a few groceries was quite terrifying; so the fact that she found herself alone in that very situation was a small triumph, filled with apprehension. Just as she was tentatively making her way to the checkout, she met the neighbour in whom she had confided. Instead of the thrill of support she hoped to feel, Kath's already ebbing confidence was shattered by the neighbour's exclamation: 'Good Lord, Kath, you shouldn't be shopping in here — you're agoraphobic!'

Those of us listening when this story was recounted were amused as we pictured a sea of confusion between agoraphobia and kleptomania. In this case it was interpreted that an agoraphobic person *shouldn't* go out into a shop, (was she going to *steal* something?) where the difficulty lies in the agoraphobic person's aversion to going out anywhere at all.

Until I confided in my friend mentioned previously, my husband had really been my only confidant. The confidence I gained from speaking with another prompted me to tell more of our friends of my fear, one of whom deserves special mention. He is a man gifted with a lively personality and during those years he was of great help to me. We shared the same sense of humour and I was able to laugh, sometimes, at my fear. He kept me in touch with reality and broadened my horizons at a time when it could have been easy to forget what life was about. He also strongly encouraged me to positively redirect my way of thinking.

This friend would phone me frequently, usually in the morning when

I had the tasks of the day ahead of me. I never once put down the receiver after that call without feeling encouraged and optimistic. He was something of an actor and an excellent mimic, and his calls would be lengthy and contain outrageous jokes and stories, nonsense conversations and serious conversations, but he was always positive. He was a lecturer at a university, and on at least three occasions, as a 'therapeutic' task, he coerced me into driving there — quite a distance from my home, and an extremely threatening trip for me to tackle. The idea was that I would meet him at an appointed place, we would go on a tour of the university, have coffee together and I would drive home again   a simple enough thing to do, for anyone who is not afraid of leaving home.

I remember the first occasion very clearly and as a very happy memory, although it was a tremendous ordeal for me. I was dreading going through with it, but I had promised I would be there, so I had no choice but to go. Anyway, I *wanted* to do it. It was almost as if the achievement of that small objective was proof of my own capability. So, although I was extremely nervous and anxious, I was also feeling the excitement of anticipation. To allay my fear of leaving the house, I kept telling myself that I was being ridiculous, I would not suffer that attack I dreaded, I would not get lost or become involved in an accident, nothing out there could hurt me, and anyway I would be safely met upon my arrival. If I had been attempting my first overseas flight alone to the most remote corner of the world where nobody spoke my language, I could not have been more apprehensive. I remember arranging to have someone mind the children and felt rather as if I were going to my doom. But I had to do it, and I had to do it with style. I even recall what I wore, and I dressed painstakingly for that little occasion, with attention to every detail; I had to boost every scrap of confidence I could find.

Finally I was on my way. Of course, once I had driven for a while, I calmed down and as no feelings of panic had arisen I began to enjoy the challenge. It helped tremendously to know that the person who in this instance was my security was waiting for me at the end of the journey. However, it was still a rather shaky woman who parked her car in an area that she had not been near for at least six years. Just the same, I was very pleased with myself; the first half of my goal for that day had been achieved and that alone was far more than I had attempted in those years.

For the next hour or two I played the role of tourist with my friend acting as an exaggerated and ridiculous guide. There was much hilarity from both of us at the expense of my predicament, for the agoraphobic never relinquishes that hold on the knowledge that he or she is away from home and safety. Therefore, every so often I would interrupt his description of our surroundings with an exclamation such as:

'What will I do if the car breaks down on the way home?' Or: 'My legs are shaking so much, I can't possibly walk up those stairs!'

My friend was very patient, but he insisted that I had to complete the whole deal. There was to be no opting out and no short cuts. When we finally sat down to coffee, my head was spinning, and my heart was pounding so much with fear that I felt sure it could be heard by people blocks away. It was then that I wanted to run in panic, for I felt I had forced myself as far as I could go and my desire was to be home in familiar surroundings. But I had nowhere to run, except to the car, which I still had to drive home. So somehow I managed to finish my coffee, we completed our tour and I was accompanied back to where I had parked the car. The car, my security, immediately relieved my anxious feelings and I drove home, elatedly. As I pulled into the drive, my gladness became tinged with regret that it was all over. It had been an occasion of fun — an excuse designed to extract me from the house on my own and throw my fear over-board, and I had survived it; something I thought I could not do.

Over the next few months, we repeated the same outing with a similar mixture of success and failure: success because at least I managed to go through with those excursions, and failure because I couldn't do it unsupported.

The positive attitude of this particular friend made me achieve something which otherwise I would never have attempted. Knowing he knew and could comprehend my plight, that he would be there to meet me and that he would phone to make sure I had arrived home safely afterwards, gave me just enough confidence to go through with it. His help amounted to cognitive behavioural therapy (CBT), which is practised and advocated widely by many health professionals today. The fact that the person supporting me in this instance was also a personal friend made it unique. In other words, I trusted him, and he imposed a discipline on me in the hope that, through it, I would overcome my fear.

Though my husband filled this supportive role tirelessly, one might expect the involvement of a person outside the family to have a greater effect. But the 'treatment' *didn't* solve my problem, for as soon as I had to face leaving the house without his creative support, my paralysing fear rose up once more. However, the generous help of this person certainly kept hope alive and I think that's what friends are for. If he should read this, I trust he will now know my eternal gratitude and thanks for his understanding.

So it *can* be worthwhile to confide in others; it is not so difficult to know upon whom to rely if we choose with care.

The *Desiderata* of the seventeenth century may not be the greatest literary work ever preserved, but it is rich in common sense – always useful in facing decisions:

> As far as possible without surrender be on good terms
> with all persons.
> Speak your truth quietly and clearly; and listen to others,
> even the dull and ignorant; they too have their story.
> Avoid loud and aggressive persons; they are vexations to the spirit.

Some inspiration perhaps, in your quest for support?

On two occasions during my life as a single woman I happened to work for two very significant men. The first was an Englishman, resident in Australia, who was internationally honoured and respected in theatrical, military and business circles. I was his PA for nearly three years. The second was the founder of the company — an empire-builder — who visited his Australian office for a few weeks on a working tour. I was chosen to assist him during his stay. In both these men I recognised one fine and noticeable quality — true humility. The point of this recollection is that first impressions of people are rarely wrong. We can know someone for only days or we can know someone for many years, but the truth of the inner person shines clearly from the outset of the meeting. We can be sure, then, that even the least of great people will always respond in a manner true to themselves. Such a person is the one in whom to confide.

It is also true that by looking beyond ourselves and by listening and hearing the needs of others we can offer our support and possibly be helped in return. If we feel afraid, we should be able to say to another person without shame: 'I am uncomfortable in this situation;' or 'I don't like elevators; would you mind if we took the stairs?' That person should be able to accept the request graciously in the knowledge that he or she one day may feel the same.

And if we do experience an apparent rejection, it is better not to be so deterred that we will not approach someone else — or even try the same person again in the hope that wisdom has been gained.

There will always be people in the world who need assistance for the practical things of life. Their form of suffering is easily recognised. But there will also always be people who need assistance and support in less obvious ways, centred within their emotional difficulties. This is an area where others may feel uncomfortable, areas from which others may choose to draw away. Generally, we still have much to learn about human emotion, how we can relate to each other at that level and how we may help each other and relieve at least some of the many complications that emotional problems produce. Yes, for the agoraphobic there is risk involved in opening oneself to our friends. But the rewards of sharing at that level are huge and well worth the risk. Those who intentionally or unintentionally cause hurt to a fear-filled person by their rebuff are possibly feeling equally anxious and ill-at-ease, but for a very different reason.

A friend is someone upon whom we can depend, someone in whom we can confide, someone we can trust and someone who accepts us for who and what we are.

Every person is of value and we each have much to give and much to receive. Who knows, some day someone we care about may need our assistance, and if we haven't learned to share our needs and our feelings, we may be denying ourselves — and our friends — the opportunity to experience the essence of that genuine love.

Chapter 7

THOSE NEGATIVE EMOTIONS

🌿

Pale Anguish keeps the heavy gate and the
warder is Despair.

Oscar Wilde

For the anxious, agoraphobic person, fear — at this level — becomes a fortress securely imprisoning its captives and elaborately crowding their awareness with an abundance of negative emotions.

First, it is with something of a jolt that he or she will realise that a huge chunk of independence has been lost.

As I write this from a secluded position on the veranda, I am watching a family of wrens busily searching for food in the soft grass under some melaleuca bushes. Although the air is close, muggy with January heat, it is still cool and damp under the trees from night rain and there is plenty of food for the birds. The parents are tending to their chicks, all chirping happily. Two in particular have my attention; the bright male with his blue cap and shiny black breast and the tiny brown baby, so totally dependent.

In the beginning, like the birds, we are all of necessity, totally dependent. Dependency can be an emotion, a need, a habit and an addiction. It can be healthy — or not. To some extent throughout our lives we are dependent on others and that's OK. People need companionship, love, the sharing of joys and sorrows, the celebration of achievements which might be meaningless if not accomplished while in interaction with others ... and so on. And in practical ways, also, people need each other. We all know how great it feels to depend occasionally on someone near to us; the caring if we are unwell, or the task done for us when time is short. But while this kind of dependence will boost our morale, the feeling of being absolutely dependent shatters it. And that's the kind of dependency I refer to here — the *dependency* attached to *submission*, and *loss*.

ke her leg very badly in a skiing accident and was in
s, dependent on others for a great deal of assistance.
k healed, the plaster was removed and, after a time of
‿aution, she was free again. The agoraphobic person becomes
‿‿nologically dependent as if there is a plaster cast on their spontaneity. Yet there is no plaster to be seen (for who can bandage the mind?),
he or she has submitted to a lesser way of life (parent, husband, wife, or
friend become the crutches) and loss (without concrete evidence of such)
becomes a daily companion.

The agoraphobic seems to be continually complicating life for those
closest because of the need to have that support person nearby whenever
he or she is away from the safety of home. If the support person is out
of view for perhaps only a few minutes, the symptoms of fear will surely
begin to arise. Like other relationship 'dances' this interaction takes on
a life of its own and presents difficulties for both parties. The support
person feels continually obliged to be at hand, and though unwillingly,
the agoraphobic person needs the other's regular presence. Understandably conflicts between the two can arise, and mutual resentment bubbles
under the surface of the relationship as tensions increase, giving rise to
the potential for inflammatory discord. Needless to say, the desperate dependency of one can lessen any hope of situational enjoyment for either
person.

Though it may seem absurd, an anxious mother can be similarly dependent upon even a very young child. It is hoped that the child will
never know the mother's need and his or her contribution to supporting it: but unless this situation improves, one can envisage many issues
arising in the future and the possibility of tragic ramifications within a
dependent relationship of that kind.

As well as dependency on other people, the agoraphobic depends on
other forms of support: the car would probably rank next in importance
– parked where it can easily be seen and readily reached. And then there
is dependency upon the functional mechanism of the vehicle as an immediate means of taking control and escaping quickly from any situation
of encroaching panic. . . someone has to ensure this is up to date.

Dependency links itself to other objects. A woman with agoraphobia will not wish to be parted from her handbag. Therein dwells her identity, her sense of security. One described her giant tote, containing anything she could possibly need for almost any emergency: aspirin for a headache, tranquillisers in case she panics, a hat in case the sun comes out, an umbrella in case it rains, scissors, needles and thread and so on. I wouldn't have been surprised if she had added that the bag itself could unfold to make a sleeping bag. Irrational? Perhaps so, but at least these dependencies are harmless, and she needs to know that she has them all with her before facing the world, as they help her keep anxiety at bay. Others of a more old-world bent may add a small bottle, carefully filled with their favorite spirit to provide another form of security. And although the bottle may never be opened, the individual depends upon its being there. And these dependencies teach us why alcohol and drugs (prescription or illicit) have become major issues for concern in the modern world. Too much stress — and no effective stress management?

The agoraphobic who is able to work beyond the confines of home knows another kind of dependency: they depend upon the tolerance and understanding of the employer or workplace associates. If fear leads to constraint in executing an individual's occupation or professional responsibilities, or if this predicament is not understood and tolerated by others, employment is obviously threatened. Many have lost their career or had opportunities stifled due to the dependent aspects and consequences of high levels of anxiety. So anxiety at this level leads to loss, conflict, resentment and dissension and these become repetitive themes to face daily.

While those with agoraphobia who are part of the workforce are under more strain than the next person, the advantages of occupation — once the ordeal of travelling is manoeuvred — are immensely helpful to the condition. More than the obvious advantages of income and personal satisfaction, within the workplace there is mental stimulus, people with whom to communicate, a sense of accomplishment and a necessary distraction from the weight of one's own struggle. All of this activity can help to provide times where 'normality' seems to have at least temporarily returned. However, anxious people depend upon a kind of rigidity within the confines of the workplace locality and generally resist the desire to join colleagues in socialising after hours. Though it fosters isolation and therefore the emotion of loneliness, there seems to be security in routine and predictable surroundings and to step outside of those could be to tempt fate and attract that dreaded panic attack.

Adolescents who are highly anxious and who develop agoraphobic reactions may easily be misunderstood. These young people depend upon the love, trust and understanding of their parents, who may take their unwillingness to leave the house for laziness or a lack of appreciation or interest in life. And while their peer group may try to assist, they cannot always be depended upon, for there are too many good things enticing them from staying at home with their anxious friend. So these fledglings, at a time of life that flaunts independence, may find themselves unproductive, helpless again, devoid of explanation and heading, perhaps for depression with the possibility of harmful dependencies in a bid for relief. And thus need and depression join the list of negative emotions.

As agoraphobia is built upon those memories and failures from previous occasions when panic occurred, the agoraphobic person will also depend upon circumstance. In anticipation of fear, if a place about to be visited does not turn out to be as pictured in the apprehensive mind's eye, he or she will be very uncomfortable, at least for some time after arrival. This dependence upon circumstances being favourable puts a special dread on having to attend a function such as a wedding or a large formal dinner where the guests' seating will have been prearranged. In such an instance the anxious person may feel even more so if placed among unfamiliar people at a circular table in the centre of a vast space — and a long way from the exit. Then again, if the seating is *not* prearranged, anxious people can feel abandoned in some kind of social limbo. A certain kind of 'strategic planning' comes into the picture just to live a single day! This means the mind is never at ease and emotional tension is ever-present.

Planning for circumstance plays a large part in the lives of the anxious, leading to other types of dependency. Those who fear the confines of public transport depend on others to drive them here and there. And, in reverse, those who are more comfortable travelling by public transport depend upon a reliable taxi service or secure departure and arrival via trams, trains or buses. These people are constantly on edge, clock-watching and arranging their activities to fit in with other people or specific timetables.

The woman who can only shop by telephone (or these days, online) depends upon the delivery person to have her goods there when she needs them. That service was vital to my own requirements — and due to certain mishaps I became a great improviser, although my family can still remind me that rice is no real substitute for potatoes!

The second big negative emotion that emerges is *loneliness*. The agoraphobic especially, can feel very lonely even when surrounded by many. Most people have glimpsed that feeling at some time in life. My earliest recollection of that type of loneliness comes from a moment when as a small child in a big playground I was caught up in a game of 'chasey'. I was 'it' and no matter how hard I tried I could not catch another child to replace me. I felt very lonely indeed until a little friend, kindly recognising my plight, volunteered to take my place. She is still a close friend to this day, and although I'm sure she thought no more of that incident, I will never forget it, for to be rescued from loneliness is a memorable event.

Because a highly anxious person will only attempt those things that he or she absolutely can do, he or she will be lonely in day-to-day life. As we can see, it is not easy, sometimes just impossible, to impulsively drop in on the person next door. Hence the agoraphobic will observe the daily routine of neighbours and friends and feel absent, even invisible. Though welcome on countless occasions to participate, and wanting so much to do so, unless the support person is included, he or she will generally take a rain check, preoccupied in dread by the embarrassing prospect of collapsing in panic. If the courage is found to execute such an adventure it will have been very well-planned.

In the years when I was a captive of fear, I was also a busy mum with the part-advantage/part-not-so, of remaining at home within that role. But the *imposed* fear keeping me there regardless of other duties was when loneliness touched me most deeply. You hear of others making their way again in the workplace, and observe people shopping, meeting socially, off to golf or tennis, back at uni completing a degree and driving freely wherever they wish. But you know that you are deprived of these activities and that if you try to engage in these natural pursuits, you will be so distracted by fear that elusive ease and the enjoyment and freedom you crave will be minimal at the very least. Distress will fill the day as feelings of sadness and helplessness surface.

This way of life means that friendships are restricted and life development is hindered through lack of regular and consistent contact. Often during those years I cancelled arrangements with some excuse because I couldn't force myself to go forward, only to spend the rest of the day sobbing my heart out and envying bitterly those who enjoyed the event. Then, of course, having failed again, the potential for panic on each subsequent occasion is reinforced.

The person with agoraphobia who lives alone and has no career or occupation outside the home to inspire any level of motivation can become severely withdrawn and subsequently depressed. As fear has created a situation where staying safely at home is the best option, this social seclusion merely exacerbates the existing problem. Though this may sound a little ruthless, it is advisable for such people to *invent* the necessary motivational need. If the situation is to improve, one must be courageous enough to initiate some changes — which is where lost confidence presents such a problem. But it's possible to start small! A lonely, middle-aged man living this way took on the responsibility of a new puppy. He grew fond of the dog, and since its life depended upon him, he became more able to go beyond fear to care for his pet. One helped the other as the animal became a surrogate support person, giving confidence to its master.

And so the emotions surrounding *loneliness* are added to the cluster of emotions surrounding *dependency* while fear continues to thrive.

The next persistent negative emotion is that of *guilt*. We can see how, through dependence upon those who care, the agoraphobic appears to be always inconveniencing other people. All these examples discussed above will then incite guilt if allowed, and so people try to compensate by being too obliging or pleasing, by outrageously spoiling the kids, by putting oneself down, by working longer hours, by burying one's head in the sand, by not properly communicating, by worrying too much, by feeling indulged, by 'beating ourselves up', by being self critical. . . there are many, many things to prompt guilt and a variety of ways to try to appease that guilt.

One woman, a seamstress, created so many new clothes for her children that it was just impossible for them to wear them all. Another compensated her partner for his patience by mowing the lawns, chopping wood and fulfilling many other chores that usually (maybe less so these days!) he would have expected to be responsible for. Not being as energetic as she, I became a prolific cake baker!

Then along with *guilt*, the emotions of *self-pity, resentment, anger and frustration* appear: 'Why did this have to happen to me?' 'Is this what life is all about? Constant fear? Others are so much worse off ! Why can't I count my blessings and get on with it all?'. . . and so on. And then frustration increases because we know that if we were not blocked by that indiscernible obstacle of fear, we would be out in the world, participating and making a worthwhile contribution to life. Life is effectively on hold, action is suspended, fear is keeping its victim confined.

It is at a time such as this that a person will make that supreme effort to achieve something alone. Fear has been dominating life for some time; he or she is sustaining many negative emotions and *despair*, creeping through cracks in the armour, hints that the situation will never recover. It feels necessary to prove oneself as a capable and companionable person. So in desperation, feeling pressured and propelled by ever increasing tension, an attempt is made to tackle the situation most feared in the hope that grim determination alone will lead to liberation. Quite probably, instead of proving anything and finding relief, the anxiety and its symptoms will be so great that the sufferer will assume that his or her condition is now worsening — a prospect too alarming to barely contemplate.

It is clear that such an incident will be very painful, surrounded by humiliation, bitter disappointment and a sense of utter failure. Defeated by these complex feelings, the person may now cease trying at all and resume the patterns of avoidance and withdrawal in the mistaken belief that these are the only reliable measures of self-protection.

The irony of these measures is that relief is only temporary and life will soon issue another predicament to face. So the negative emotions burn brighter, self-doubt, and low self-esteem join the rest and tears flow —

together with an evaluation that 'everyone else is so normal — why not me?'

This is a moment to reflect that anxious people generally have high standards and self expectations. What is 'normal' to the anxious person may be well above what is normal to others and they should remember that people are people — with varying degrees of ability, intelligence and soul — while the word 'normal' is an over-rated mystery.

Since all these negative emotions are a part of fear and the experience of each of them aggravates fear, life becomes increasingly complicated. As noted already, many people become deeply depressed and largely incapacitated by their struggle with anxiety. In that regard I was less affected perhaps than some but I stood in similar shoes and I know that painful, painful pain too well.

And then other fears arise. Two good examples would be fear of losing the support person one way or another, and fear of the difficulties of agoraphobia if facing old age. When feeling constantly open to attack because of blow after blow of what is deemed to be failure, one of my own worries was that as I seemed so incompetent for the greater part of my life how would I cope if faced with a real reason for fear? When contemplating other worries in life one begins to wonder just how much we can take . . . or, for that matter, give.

I used to raise these issues during psychoanalysis to ease my concern and the psychiatrist assured me time and again that these aspects of fear were unfounded. In his opinion, I was a strong and stable person who would always manage life well. Though at that time I remained unconvinced, I had to admit that my concern for long-term susceptibility came from the fact that the anxious mind fosters all aspects of insecurity and my anxiety — or *fear* — was very high. To handle that, I tried not to think of the future at all!

In seeking help or advice, the sufferer will inevitably receive facile advice — 'try not to worry' and 'keep occupied'. These seem like reasonable remarks until we stop to consider that worry is a fundamental expression of fear and in order to become occupied effectively it is usually necessary to step out into that world which poses such a threat. These recommendations simply feed back to guilt and provoke more resentment, anger and frustration. The individual knows only too well that he or she would be capable of a great deal if not for this stranglehold of fear and the personal inadequacy surrounding it.

With anxiety having long left me, it is challenging to recall such intense insecurity. But I certainly ran the gamut of all of those reactions. Thus *anguish* feels like a very good word to summarise the intricate negative emotions surrounding anxiety.

And so, despairingly and like many, I had learned to *live fearfully*. But that is indeed second-class living; the overall sense of loss, of missing so much in life and the disappointment surrounding that eternal guard on spontaneous existence. For you know, however hard you fight or try, that as soon as you reach the threshold, your heart will start to thump, your legs will turn to jelly and you realise that fear has imprisoned the reality of *your-self*.

Chapter 8

PERSEVERANCE

🌿

Perseverance, dear my Lord
Keeps honour bright: to have done is to hang
Quite out of fashion, like a rusty mail
In monumental mockery.

Shakespeare

Probably I am a rather determined person, but in all this dreadful maze of fear and the side-effects of it, I had one ambition: to get out of it.

As my life prior to this happening had been spent in doing outgoing things, and my greatest youthful dream then had been the world of music and the stage, my present behaviour was paradoxical. I had never been afraid like this. Why was I so afraid now of something, which I couldn't even identify, that prevented me from living life with freedom? Fear was dominating my life and taking with it all my hopes and ambitions. It annoyed me greatly to think that something could have such power over me, and because of it, I had lost confidence in myself and suffered also loss of self-esteem and spontaneity. So I wanted very much to continue to seek any form of help that was available which might enable me to enjoy life again.

However, I began to realise that the manner by which I was endeavouring to overcome this problem was causing me yet another problem. With psychoanalysis, there is little one can 'do' in the strict sense of the word. Liberation from the problem in hand should apparently just happen, as a result of talking and trying to relate times of anxiety to other situations which have occurred in life. Then, we hope, one day the pieces of the puzzle will fall into place. Some past event of significance will be discussed freely enough to be consciously revealed. From this insight, the inhibiting anxiety symptoms should gradually disappear.

This seemed to me always to be a very vague and slow solution to my fear of leaving my home. For my life was happy! I was not living with any obvious major problem or stressful situation to cause anxiety — but there existed a barrier of fear through which I couldn't pass. So, in an attempt to hasten this remedy, I tried very hard to associate the occasions when I felt most afraid with the circumstances in which these occasions occurred. But the answer was always the same: my anxiety symptoms were primarily and powerfully connected with having to leave the house or be away from the security on which I depended.

Here then, was my new problem. I found that, added to my loss of spontaneity due to my fear, I also had a guard on my natural emotional reactions. I found myself trying too hard to analyse why I had felt uncomfortable in that particular street, shop or house; or why I did not feel edgy at one particular gathering of a group of friends, yet at another gathering with people from the same party, feelings of panic had arisen. Thus I was constantly on the lookout for symptoms — which of course increased the likelihood of such feelings occurring. These ruminations also had the effect of preventing me from deliberately inviting an excursion to where I had experienced symptoms previously, in case they arose again under the repeated circumstances. Very complicated!

As I didn't speak openly about these thoughts, fortunately it was primarily only myself, and occasionally my husband, who suffered the monotony of them. But I would always recall such ideas to the psychiatrist and we would try to relate all these instances to the rest of my life, or he would again raise the subject of my suppressed anger and I would go home more puzzled than ever.

Thus far, neither this expert nor I had been able to access the source of either my supposed anger *or* my ever-present anxiety by means of the usual psychoanalytic/therapeutic discussion. So it was recommended that I participate in a therapy session, accompanied by a sedating, truth-revealing cocktail — a mixture of Amytal and Ritalin administered intravenously. This was a dreary day-long experience in an old and gloomy hospital and no amazing 'truth' came forth. The occasion was made memorable for me only because after the session, I was left to sleep off the drug, waking a little later to find teeming rain hammering through the decrepit ceiling, practically drowning me there in my bed! Once again, my enjoyment of the ridiculous salvaged the moment.

If instead of such measures, a clear explanation had been proffered to help me understand that the symptoms I lived in fear of and the attack I dreaded were largely produced by my own tension — an automatic (though negative) defence — at least I may have begun to see the wood for the trees. But in constantly analysing my feelings and searching for their cause by fair means or foul, I was magnifying my fear and unintentionally keeping *tension* at peak level.

During this period of my life, I read many books on the subject of anxiety. Most of the material available at that time did not seem to recognise my specific fear and the majority of works were technical and therefore of little support to me. I found clinical books lacked the comfort of intimacy, leaving me, the reader, feeling very much removed from the writer and more mortified and alone than ever. Many books and articles advocated the overcoming of fear by force (in other words, various forms of exposure to fear); these usually had the effect of increasing rather than decreasing my anxiety. Anyway, I had tried this formula already in the kindest way possible and to no avail. When one can be overwrought by the very thought of going out unaccompanied, reading material such as that is of little assistance. I also found little by way of lucid explanation of the condition and never a relatively basic solution to the problem.

Eventually I came across one book in which, although it was written primarily about more severe mental conditions, the author did touch on the initial symptoms of fear. From this book I finally learned that the attack which I spent my life trying to avoid was in fact *panic*. I also learned at last that the initial symptoms of that attack were caused by the rush of adrenaline which is the body's natural and automatic response to an emergency.

How strange that I had to discover this information myself and that no experienced 'other' had been able to define my situation adequately. Knowledge at least brought some explanation and a little less dread of the symptoms themselves. But I still didn't understand why I continued to experience the symptoms, and nor could I comprehend from the book how I could prevent them and be free from fear.

Around this time, a friend, in whom I had confided, told me she knew someone else with my fear, and that it was known as 'agoraphobia'.

Now at least I could identify my difficulty! Yet, with this information and the continuing search through the past, there still seemed to be little hope of losing either the symptoms or the fear of them.

As a result of my newfound knowledge, I then pushed myself further to attend courses run by organisations specialising in human development. These included behavioural therapy, discussion sessions, Yoga and several varieties of relaxation techniques. Nothing changed, and leaving the house to attend any of these options remained the outward face of the ongoing problem.

The treatment had now gone into several years and I was still living in fear, experiencing the same feelings over and over again. The strain of keeping appointments with the psychiatrist was as great as ever, and no escape was forthcoming. By now it was his belief that my anxiety had not originated from some traumatic event in early life — of course I already knew this — so presumably the *level* of my anxiety couldn't possibly be that severe. Therefore, if we could just persist in seeking *something* — some incident or sequence of events that was keeping my anxiety alive, the condition would improve. . .

Though this opinion should have provided encouragement rather, through the ever-present symptoms, it increased the frustration and ridiculousness of the situation. I also began to feel certain of a lack of comprehension on his part and my confidence in this treatment approach began to seriously wane. All I wanted was to be able to walk out my front door and live freely and naturally without constantly experiencing enough rising panic to justify confronting an approaching herd of wild elephants! How could those symptoms experienced in the local shops, or even just the thought of boarding a tram, be so dramatically linked to some unrecognised incident from my past? I began to wonder whether there was any point in continuing with this treatment. I had tried what seemed to be everything to overcome agoraphobia. There was apparently nothing beneficial left to explore, and I had virtually accepted the problem, at great cost to my personal enjoyment of life.

At this time, the psychiatrist suggested I become part of one of his therapy groups. Again, willing to try anything, I made myself go — with my husband waiting for me in the car, of course, or a taxi there and back again.

The therapy groups were worse. I experienced all the symptoms of panic, all the apprehension of leaving the house to keep the appointments, plus the emotions of several other people as well. Their needs seemed so much more important and their problems much more dramatic than mine. Within that group were discussed issues that included dark depression, sexual deviance, attempted murder and suicide. Within this situation, my eyes were opened a little more to the challenges of the wider world. But my fear of leaving the safety of home paled into insignificance beside the disturbing events that had affected the members of that group – and I am sure most had no understanding of the difficulty I regularly faced. I remember those sessions as if one had suddenly landed as an intruder in another world; the atmosphere was filled with intensity and introspection, there was a distinct lack of humour or optimism and there was very little feeling of hope. I felt out of place in that environment and exhausted from fighting my own constant apprehension. So from the moment of arrival I would be preoccupied with controlling my rising symptoms and unable to contribute greatly to the group as a whole.

Nevertheless I persevered – though it was obvious that others present could not embrace the trouble I had attending the sessions – and that just *being* there was the primary issue. Later, having become a psychotherapist myself, I know that this could have been a very useful part of my journey had I not been so terribly tense – and had the therapist had the knowledge and skills to address that part of my problem first and foremost. But that did not happen and the final frustration in that phase of treatment came when one of the group members asked me quite aggressively: 'What are you doing here anyway?' I had on several occasions, so I believed, attempted to explain my predicament. Yet still none of the participants there could see it as an obstacle for concern. I left in a flood of tears, privately vowing never to return.

I decided some time after my experience in group therapy that I had had enough of psychoanalysis, at least for the present.

I was, at this stage, about six months pregnant with our fourth child and could see no way to freedom from agoraphobia. I had lived the last few years accompanied by fear, so apparently I must continue that way.

To some extent analysis had been interesting, as it explored the regions of the past and attempted to associate past with present-day life. However, I seemed to be going round and round in circles and making no progress to end the confusion. All in all, I was totally frustrated by this endless and seemingly pointless search that was absorbing much of my energy.

Out of five years of psychiatric assistance came very little, I think. The anxiety had lessened only to the extent that my life appeared normal to the rest of the world. However, I'm sure that any improvement was due more to the passing of time and the fact that, although virtually housebound, I had always remained very much involved in life. The psychoanalytic model and the psychiatrist's model for psychotherapy was at no time able to reveal any unresolved issues or significant events, past or present, great enough to justify eight years of anxiety compelling enough to produce agoraphobia.

I made no further appointments with the psychiatrist, more or less believing that this problem was something I would just have to live with. Though those years of therapy were filled with confusion and disappointment I have the greatest respect for that doctor and I am grateful for the many hours he spent listening to me and offering reassurance. I do not intend my comments to display a lack of appreciation of his skills or assistance. But he just didn't 'get it'! The psychiatric model generally is often surprisingly unable to offer effective measures for overcoming this kind of fear.

And right then I *almost* gave up any hope of recovery. I almost accepted that I would live the rest of my life only able to move uncomfortably within that restricted radius of my home, depending in all other instances upon the companionship of my husband. However, as my older children were now approaching their teenage years, I wished to be able to participate in their lives fully as a mother wants to do.

Somewhere, deep inside me, was my faithful friend: perseverance. I knew there had to be a satisfactory answer.

PART TWO

Stillness Meditation

Chapter 9

THE INTERVENTION OF DESTINY

Happy is the Man that findeth wisdom and the
Man that getteth understanding.

Proverbs

It is certain that the path upon which Destiny leads us is never clearly defined; it is also often bumpy and seems to be leading nowhere. Then suddenly and surprisingly we arrive at an intersection at which point we must make a choice, a choice which may put meaning into all that has gone before. There is indeed, a time for everything.

In those preceding eight years, I had sought the best of help and treatment that I knew to be available to overcome my fear. Now my fourth child was to be born and of course I was dreading leaving home, the stay in hospital and so on, but I had been through that before in a highly anxious state and survived. Our first three children had been delivered very easily, but because of a complicated miscarriage between my third child and this pregnancy, I was apprehensive of the actual birth in a way that I had not experienced on those occasions.

As mentioned earlier, I had read many books dealing with anxiety. Out of all those books the one which impressed me most was *Relief Without Drugs*, the first of many self-help books published by Dr Ainslie Meares, the eminent Melbourne psychiatrist. Now a classic, this book intimates with sincerity the author's profound and sensitive insight into human emotions, and the difficulties people can be confronted with due to the influence of anxiety and tension upon their lives. In this book the author teaches his unique style of 'meditation' — at that time described as 'relaxing mental exercises', a positive and natural life-skill for the relief of tension, pain and anxiety.

In my search for a particular kind of reassurance at that time, I re-read the section in *Relief Without Drugs* which deals with childbirth. I thought about Meares' ideas a great deal. What was said clearly in black and white somehow made more impression upon me then than did any former relaxation technique to which I had been exposed. I re-read his entire book.

When I had read that book previously in my search to overcome fear, I have to admit that I didn't accept his advice. I did not believe in relaxation of any kind — I had experimented already with a range of similar techniques and no improvement to my state of fear had come from these. And I was still so involved in trying to overcome fear by other means that Dr Meares' ideas seemed altogether too simple to be effective. Also, I felt that I was missing some vital point in his message, and therefore had no hope of achieving what he recommended, or changing in any way by attempting those recommendations.

At this stage, it was the birth of a baby, not so much the agoraphobia, that was foremost in my mind. I was prepared to try to do as described in that chapter to allay my apprehension of the delivery. I practised as described in the book and pictured myself in the situation, all the time telling myself to release tension. When the time for delivery came I very much had the idea of *physical* relaxation, and to my amazement and delight, the birth of our younger son was completely free of distress and without drugs of any kind. This was the first time in my life that I really appreciated what *relaxation* meant — and took it seriously.

The experience impressed me tremendously. If being aware of tension and knowing how to release it could remove the apprehension which contributed to pain in childbirth, then I felt there must be something more in this doctor's idea. I was still desperate to conquer agoraphobia, and yet I was also well aware of the fact that if I investigated his teaching further I could be about to embark upon one more lengthy project which would yet again amount to nothing. Having experienced success with physical relaxation, it seemed sensible at least to take this a step further. As I wanted to understand completely how *mental* relaxation was achieved, I decided to write to Dr Meares. I told him of my recent experience and asked if he could help me to overcome my fear of leaving the safety of home.

Dr Meares' reply invited me to attend one of the large group sessions he was holding at that time to instruct people in the experience of his teaching. I was pleased to receive this ready response, but of course I had all the usual trouble leaving the house, taking a taxi to the city and arranging for one to bring me home again — together with the immense apprehension and insecurity that was my constant companion when out of the house.

However, when I arrived at my destination, I was immediately relieved by the sense of ease — a quiet, almost sacred environment welcomed me, despite there being such a large number of people gathered together. I felt reasonably comfortable there. But I have to admit that my first attempt to experience mental relaxation was not very satisfactory. The fact that I was away from home and alone in new surroundings, together with the experience of something so different, created such concern within me that I found it quite difficult to close my eyes for more than a few moments at a time. I was far from relaxed, so I spent the time wishing the event would soon be over. The prospect of another such visit did not please me, but I felt I should persevere a little more as this appeared to be my last hope of freedom from fear.

I arranged to see Dr Meares privately, which gave me the opportunity to discuss with him personally the fear I had lived with for the past eight years. I needed this personal contact and his reassurance, for I still believed I was the sole possessor of such a ridiculous fear.

As already explained, the task of keeping appointments and waiting for extended periods of time is sheer torture to a person whose anxiety has reached phobic proportions. I remember noting with some relief that I was kept only a very few minutes in his reception area. I also noticed a rare tranquillity in the atmosphere; a pleasant efficient orderliness in mellow surroundings, and a vase of perfumed jasmine on his secretary's desk.

Dr Meares listened to my story. There was no lengthy discussion as to the cause of my constant fear. There was no mention of psychoanalysis or any wandering into the past. Dr Meares had, by this time, separated himself from mainstream psychiatry, working outside the conventional framework of medicine. Therefore he no longer recommended or prescribed medication. While he mentioned that the practice of his method of mental relaxation would replace all need for medication, he did not insist that I either take or not take tablets. There was no suggestion that I must make myself overcome fear or force myself in any way, and there was no dramatic diagnosis. Yet he obviously understood my difficulty and I sensed strongly that he knew exactly what I was experiencing.

In summary, he simply stated: 'You are rather tense.' And he promised me that if I accepted his idea, and learned and practised mental relaxation as he taught it, my anxiety and its accompanying tension would be greatly reduced, the persistent symptoms which caused me to be afraid would disappear, and I would be free of this affliction.

On that occasion I expressed some doubt, saying to Dr Meares: 'And if I should fail?' Having tried so many ways to overcome agoraphobia, this seemed too easy and I was still concerned that freedom would elude me yet. Firmly but gently, he replied — and these are his exact words: 'There is no question of failure. Trust me.' So it was arranged that I would return in two days' time for the first of a series of group sessions in mental relaxation.

When I was home again after that discussion, I wondered about where I had been, what I had learned. I had tried for so long and in so many ways to overcome fear — was this any different? What was this doctor offering to teach me that no-one else had suggested? *Release of tension — and the relief of anxiety through bringing the mind to a state of stillness . . . a kind of meditation.* And if I did learn this meditation, how could it help me overcome that persistent phobia? Surely it was too simple for all my years of misery? Scepticism tugged at me. Was this man genuine? Were his promises to be trusted? Was I being 'taken for a ride'? Was I going to be disappointed again? And yet his attitude was calm, strong and positive and one of absolute hope. I could have wished for nothing more.

It was a glorious spring day and I walked out into the sunshine musing upon these things and wondering whether or not I had made a wise decision by committing myself to this process. As I stood there, a certain fragrance came to me and simultaneously I noticed the swirl of pink and white jasmine on my own fence. And then I remembered Nessa's garden. The peace and serenity; those precious quiet moments where tranquillity could not be shaken. The security and reassurance of that haven without fear stirred in my memory and this was the inspiration I needed to pursue my goal.

Dr Meares' promise was precisely what happened.

Initially I attended meditation sessions with Dr Meares twice weekly for about four to six weeks. I was taught to sit in slight discomfort, and to experience *without trying to do so*, a complete physical relaxation leading to, more importantly, the experience of *stillness of mind*. The first few sessions were difficult. I had believed that I could not learn to relax. I had not seen any point in relaxation of any kind, nor could I accept that pausing to relax could benefit the task of living. This was a prejudice and a mistake.

Because of that prejudice, now I had to overcome a tendency to resist the idea of 'letting go'. I was being taught to 'go with' rather than fight against disturbing thoughts and feelings. To allow this approach to occur, it was necessary during my early sessions *consciously* to let go of physical tension. Dr Meares intimated that the release of physical tension must come first; ease within the body would lead to ease within the mind. This too, was to be simple in its execution. There was none of the usual progressive muscle relaxation – just the simple acceptance of one's natural human ability to relax. . . to let go!

He also indicated that release of tension is particularly important where the muscles of the face are concerned and especially the muscles of the forehead, as 'the smoothing out of the forehead has a stilling effect on the mind itself'. I could understand the significance of that and was soon surprised to discover just how many areas of my body were holding tension. Even more importantly, I finally began to recognise how greatly my whole being had been dominated by tension.

After a few sessions, it became easier for me to release physical tension but it was to be some time before I would experience similar release within my mind. At first I was trying to achieve this, trying too hard. I suppose I could say I over-applied myself in endeavouring to rest my mind. Utter simplicity was all that was required, without effort. But within myself I questioned myself; my thoughts and reactions as I sat there; the anxiety that welled up within me at intervals during the experience; the eerie absence of any kind of stimulus as my mind grew used to letting go. I wondered whether others found this experience the same as I did, and at times I became quite afraid. But I persevered. And over time I learned and accepted that, contrary to my former belief, there is nothing difficult about relaxation and that no harm can come from letting go of tension — in the body or in the mind. In fact, I began to acknowledge that mental rest was a natural and spontaneous function of the mind.

Dr Meares insisted that for complete effectiveness, as well as attending sessions with him, I had to practise this myself, setting aside time to deliberately re-create the experience at home a couple of times each day. Like anything that is worthwhile, the more we are prepared to put into it, the greater the result. I began to find the regular meditative experience a pleasant and rewarding addition to my daily routine. The effect of the frequent visits and my home practice was dramatic, to say the least. I was experiencing something that was most definitely new to my adult life: two hours each week of absolute stillness, as well as the times I took for daily practice. And gradually, and unbelievably, something was changing.

Supported by the repeated experience of stillness, I reminded myself to let tension go all the time: walking, talking, driving, leaving the house — even thinking about leaving the house! The symptoms I feared were becoming less intense and occurring less frequently.

Questioning myself again, I wondered whether these changes were occurring just because I was spending time in deliberate relaxation. For I was not doing anything else to subdue fear . . . the improvement was just happening, almost without any intervention. If that was the case, it had taken apparently very little by way of relaxation to reverse that fear of so many years. Why then, had the other forms of relaxation that I had attempted been ineffective?

I realised that I *was* experiencing the sense of stillness in the right way; and it *was* that experience of *stillness meditation* that was so effective, not merely the practice of physical relaxation. But while I was disputing the source of my success, the subtlety of *stillness* was being overlooked. So relaxation was the answer! But not just *any* attempt at relaxation. It was the acceptance of simplicity and the *meditative element* — the *mental relaxation* — that was the secret.

Time went by and more changes were noticeable, many of which were as subtle as the stillness itself. My first observation of these changes was quite special and here is an odd little anecdote.

Being animal lovers ourselves, our children grew up surrounded by pets. At the top of the list was the dog, in those years a standard poodle. He was a beautiful animal, chocolate brown with golden eyes. He had been part of the family for some years by then and, each morning after the older children had gone to school, Kimba would sit faithfully on the floor beside me as I read the morning paper.

On one particular morning, a few weeks after my commencement of meditation, we were sitting together as usual and Kimba snuggled closer to me and put his head on my lap. I remember looking down at him — and for the first time, I truly looked into his eyes. As if my own vision had been blind to his deeper existence, for the first time in years I saw the life within him. Tears sprang forth as in a surprising and curious way I was filled with a kind of compassion for all of life in this tender exchange of love between myself and our dog. This serendipitous moment seemed to confirm the beginning of my own transformation — as if until that instant I had been somehow lost to existence and had now been found again.

Following that experience other things came into sharper focus. It seemed that within this new capacity to be relaxed I was also experiencing a spontaneous kind of growing, coupling the ability to perceive my sur-roundings differently with a fresh appreciation of my own participation in life and a richer sense of existence. I noticed my thinking had become clearer and my concentration improved, while ideas, memories and in-sights blossomed into my awareness, bringing an understanding that had until now been absent. It was easier to be more adaptive and accommo-dating of change, or of events and situations, to be more open-minded and to be more optimistic.

Around this time I also became aware of the renewal of the gift of trust and I realised that trust was not something that had always been present in me. Doubt, somewhere so fittingly described as 'the tail of the snake', had slithered into my awareness, imposing its negative influence upon me. In this new turn of events, I had had to trust Dr Meares and his method — in fact he had asked for my trust. And, after consideration, I had given it. Now, within the experience of meditative stillness, I began to see that I had in recent years lost trust in myself. In learning now how to relax and let go into stillness, I was indirectly learning to relax into my own capability . . . to trust and let go a little in daily living. Rather like the person who must now abandon his crutches after relying upon them to walk, I was learning to abandon the doubts and crutches of my dependency.

Within the repetition of stillness my fatigue of many years vanished. For a long time all my energies had been drawn into coping with fear and managing my responsibilities as best I could. In place of exhaustion, I began to notice new energy. Young children keep their mothers very busy but the fatigue I had felt was more than that of busyness. I was not really coping well with all I had to do. Now, with my energy restored, increased stamina and a zest for life re-emerged and maintaining order was less of a chore. And there *was* more order in my life. I wasn't doing anything differently to create this — it just began to happen that I could achieve more in any day in a calm manner and with far less effort.

As I experienced and practiced *stillness meditation* more and questioned it *less*, I began to glimpse the right idea, and the experience itself became freer: the letting go of tension, the letting go of happenings around me, the pleasant feeling of deliberate effortless *being*, inwardly removed from distracting sounds, thoughts or memories. Soon, during meditation, I began to encounter a velvety stillness and an at-one-ness with my-*self* and my surroundings, very calm, very natural, a feeling which transcended discomfort of any kind. And an inner 'knowing' of the essence of the stillness and strength of life evolved — something that had not been part of my everyday expectation.

On one occasion during a meditation session at Dr Meares' rooms, I experienced feelings of panic arising. Having tasted sweet success and believing such feelings to have deserted me, this seemed like a setback and alarmed me. Dr Meares explained the incident as transient anxiety, a normal enough occurrence, which was of no consequence.

He reassured me by explaining that occasionally something like that might happen when learning meditation, because as we let go, old defences alert our subconscious mind. This alert can trigger alarm bells, causing adrenaline to be released within the body, together with the physical response to a desire to 'fight or flee'.

And so we are jolted back to reality, disconcerted and puzzled that anxiety can occur when we are meant to be relaxed. In fact, this event was an indication of progress. After years of high tension, I was now capable of relaxation! Having thus survived panic within the meditation experience, I realised I was then better equipped to let go beyond those feelings should they occur again in my everyday life. Now a new, positive response was impressed upon my subconscious mind, further replacing the anxiety response.

More than the physical energy I had regained, I found I now began not only to 'know' but to *experience* the inner strength which Dr Meares promised; with that came increased emotional security. I began to feel renewed confidence in myself generally. Thereafter, steadily and surely agoraphobia disappeared, along with all its negative complications. No longer did I feel afraid to do something or the need to fight whatever I had to do — I just calmly *did* it. I challenged myself to attempt things which would formerly have been impossible. But in doing those things I knew that I must not do them by force but 'with ease', so when faced with a shopping trip or a visit to school or a social event, I cultivated the habit of going forward easily.

Soon this habit began to replace my old ways, inviting even greater challenge. How far could I go in this manner? I was soon surprised and overjoyed to discover that I was able to drive my car to the city to attend the meditation sessions, park it some distance away and enjoy walking the rest of the way without apprehension.

So driving, even in heavy traffic, was no longer difficult. The red light was an opportunity for me to 'let go' rather than become tense against my former perception of this as an oppressive obstacle. Driving on a freeway now felt 'free' and expansive, where once I had felt controlled by such situations. I recall the first day I travelled comfortably to the city by public transport, triumphantly saying to Dr Meares upon my arrival: 'I feel that I've been dead for ages and am now reborn.'

It is important to reiterate that I had been acutely anxious for eight years. Suddenly, within less than eight weeks, with regular sessions with

Ainslie Meares, the phobia had virtually left my life. Fear, and all its unpleasant symptoms — the nausea, giddiness, unreality, apprehension — had dramatically subsided and life was taking on a finer glow. For years I had been constantly afraid of panic. Now, panic attacks simply never occurred — nor have they recurred since.

And now, with reduced tension, the picture was clear to me. I came to understand the truth of agoraphobia, that this reaction is one of defence and a habit of avoidance, built upon the habit of being tense. Therefore I no longer felt so vulnerable and if occasionally little reminder symptoms dropped into my day, I was able to dispose of them calmly without further concern until eventually they simply never occurred. The vicious circle was broken — I had only now to replace old unwanted habits with my newfound attitude of ease.

More achievements followed. I remember my elation at shopping in supermarkets without fear. Instead of avoiding items forgotten from the weekly order, or sending the children, I now had the power to choose again. The shelves of garish products glittered seductively, now that I could calmly observe and buy. To think that one could know joy from buying the groceries! And yet the happy release from that constant apprehension was so great that on my first couple of visits to large stores I found myself having to suppress my desire to laugh aloud for joy.

With each triumph over fear, I gained extra confidence. Never again did I cancel arrangements because of fear. No longer did I need to keep my husband within constant view when we were out together. It was a great thrill to enter an auditorium and not feel anxious if the seats were in the middle of the row, or think about where the exit might be. Now that I could do it, I luxuriated in the idea of impulsively driving to another suburb to shop, or simply browse — an expression of ease in itself.

Evidenced by the decline of my bank balance, fitting rooms no longer held any dread; nor did department stores, queues or waiting rooms. Open areas – like watching the kids play sport – were no longer defeating. The pleasure of the game was more important; and the beach and the countryside were glorious places to be enjoyed once more, leading eventually to the enrichment of travel throughout the world. How unbelievable that so much of life could be spoiled by fear!

I noticed too, that other little anxieties had disappeared. For example, throughout my life I had never been too keen on spiders. A spider in the room was quite disturbing for me and always meant finding someone to dispose of it. During my years of agoraphobia, a spider in the room would, to my anxious mind, assume gigantic proportions, comparable with one of the props from a Speilberg movie! As my overall tension level diminished, so did my image of spiders. If one appeared in my presence, now it was simply a spider and, if necessary, I could kindly dispose of it myself.

With new liberation the loneliness that I had felt within agoraphobia was now transformed to an appreciation of independence. Having learned to be still and to be alone with myself in this way, I became content with being alone in everyday life. Solitude became for me something to be treasured, where once to be alone would have caused me dread. From time to time I pondered the gift of solitude, aware that my endurance of agoraphobia and my overcoming of it was leading me beyond pain to greater growing discoveries and the assurance of my*self*.

Yet I also treasured the gift of company and the happy times spent together with family and friends. Without the burden of tension, my life was far more interesting, becoming busier and busier, and yet being so involved seemed quite easy.

The daily discipline of stillness and the order that flowed from that experience moved me towards other self-care routines. Regular exercise, especially a morning walk, became part of my day. It was easy to revise my diet, explore healthy alternatives and make recommended adjustments. I embraced the idea of journal writing and made time each morning for my thoughts to flow on the page. And I took up tennis again and later swimming, on a regular basis.

One of the most rewarding disciplines I then imposed upon myself was to go regularly to my husband's office. My involvement in even the most menial of tasks provided me with the opportunity to flaunt my newfound freedom in situations which had formerly generated fear. I practised the release of tension in long queues at the bank or visiting other establishments. I experienced the ridiculous joy of waiting my turn in a crowded post office!

Thus the anticipation of unpleasant symptoms lessened with every achievement. No longer did I find myself weighing the possibilities as to how I might fight my way through whatever situation I was facing — fear was fast becoming something of my past. Often the absence of fear caught me unawares and I would momentarily wonder whether I had left the house forgetting to bring with me something important. And the urge to look over my shoulder in search of my former unwelcome companion caused me some amusement from time to time.

Since energy and order now provided me with an increase in personal space, I soon yearned to pursue those other things which had been denied me for years. In the deepest part of my being, my soul, she who had been bruised and had 'slept' for a long time, gently woke and nudged me towards my need for spiritual nourishment. The time was right to satisfy some of my more personal, soul-satisfying needs. My first step in that direction led me on a special trip to a suburb some distance from home to find a particular shop which specialised in art materials; I had decided that creative expression would be a good start to fulfilling my wishes. I recall standing there in that shop, unfamiliar circumstances for me, and hardly daring to believe that it was me there, miles from home without fear. The feeling was euphoric.

But singing, my former passion, had been idle within me for too long. When the time was right, I tentatively sought a teacher. Although one-off trips to distant places were now readily carried out, I was not yet ready for a regular commitment to lessons too far from my general locality. I was fortunate to find a lady nearby, elderly, talented and somewhat eccentric, but with an exultant enthusiasm that welcomed me back to the world of music. I enjoyed about a year with her, re-learning my skills sufficiently to move further afield after her health failed and she retired from teaching. Gradually I became accomplished again. And happily, my soul danced with delight, rejoicing while immersed once again in the mystery and grace of the perfected art of other musicians. I was re-building my life from the foundations to the top floor, the stable foundation being, of course, the meditative stillness from which I was increasingly gaining strength, confidence and joy.

In recalling these significant steps to freedom, I am glossing over the most important ones; the spontaneous car trips to take the children here or there; the hours spent driving and waiting at riding lessons, swimming lessons, dancing classes; the impulsive agreements to take an enthusiastic five-year-old to see fifty cartoons. It was the little things that meant so much, now that they could be fully enjoyed once again.

So I progressed to freedom from agoraphobia — the fear of fear — even *forgetting* what it had felt like to live that way. Amazingly, all these changes commenced within a year or so of my first visit to Dr. Meares. After those early twice-weekly sessions, I attended weekly sessions at his rooms for some time, then every two weeks. Later I would visit monthly over some years, for maintenance and the reward of the deep meditation experienced in his presence. I had lived eight years in fear, at least five of which had been occupied in analysing myself to try to find the cause of that anxiety. Now I was free of this problem and the freedom had begun after only a matter of a few weeks.

I remember thanking Dr Meares for his help. His reply was: 'You really did it yourself, you know.' And he was right, for the fact remains that any achievement depends upon someone making the commitment to begin – and allowing change to follow. No matter who we are or whatever our ambition, unless we take the first step towards our goal, nothing will ever happen to alter or improve our position; and this is especially so where fear stands in our path. The whole process of dispelling fear is one of self-achievement. But one needs to be shown the way. As soon as I had the guidance from this gifted man, I could let go of the tension within me and replace it with the strength of my own tranquillity.

Destiny had taken me by the hand and I was on the right path at last.

Chapter 10

A BRIEF HISTORY AND OVERVIEW
OF STILLNESS MEDITATION

w

Some run for shelter,
The tree holds firm
And sways with the storm,
The eagle is borne higher and higher.

Ainslie Meares

With the telling of this story, first published in 1983, Dr Ainslie Meares invited me to offer my services to others as an exponent and teacher of his concept of meditation. And so I began my role as therapist. Three years later, unexpectedly, Dr Meares died; but not without leaving the legacy of his innovation — the natural management of stress and anxiety through his particular form of meditation. He was, in fact, the pioneer of therapeutic meditation, a concept which has contributed to a broader view of healing in Western society and of self-help by natural means.

The work of Ainslie Meares

Dr Meares' ideas, revolutionary in the Sixties and Seventies, alarmed many of his peers. His work was viewed at times with suspicion, sometimes with scorn, frequently with scepticism. In the days when *medication* ruled as the cure for all ills — and this had to be administered by the doctor — Ainslie Meares empowered people to help themselves through *meditation*. Those who accepted his teachings and were healed by them rose to admire him, respecting his courage, respecting his wisdom. He wrote prolifically on the subject and his numerous papers and books were published and translated throughout the world. In the latter part of his life, his discoveries relating to the practice of intensive meditation and the remission of cancer largely paved the way for more liberal advances in health care adopted by progressive medical practitioners today.

Let me backtrack for a moment to consider where his new ideas began and to present an overview of this particular style of meditation. As I was searching for a solution to my phobia, some 20 years earlier Dr Meares had begun his own search. Disillusioned with people's reliance upon sedatives and analgesics together with what he described as costly psychiatric treatment, Dr Meares sought a *natural, simple and effective way* to help his patients to find 'calm of mind and control of pain', a way of helping themselves towards a better quality of life. Dr Meares, already a distinguished psychiatrist, was also an expert in clinical hypnosis and one-time President of the International Society for Clinical and Experimental Hypnosis. His attraction to the function of the mind led him to travel the world, seeking throughout 'twenty-one lands' an understanding of the skills and abilities used by people in a variety of cultures; yogis and mystics who, through mind control over their bodies, were reputed to be practically immune to pain. His fascinating encounters he later recorded in a small book *Strange Places, Simple Truths* (Souvenir Press, London: 1969).

Impressed after first-hand contact with Eastern mystics, Dr Meares was thus inspired to experiment further. He discovered that the sensations of anxiety, tension and pain could be significantly reduced and personal ease maintained by consciously inducing a state of *mental* rest for a period of time, once or twice each day. Coupled with his scientific background and his expertise in the use of hypnosis with his patients, he then adapted his principal findings to a unique and simple method of self-help, requiring only a little patience and personal self-discipline. His first book on this subject for the general public, *Relief Without Drugs*, describes the technique he adapted from his discoveries as *relaxing mental exercises*. A later work from 1978, *The Wealth Within*, takes the reader a little further as his own ideas developed. In that work, Dr Meares coined the phrase *mental ataraxis*, meaning 'absence of disturbance in the mind', to distinguish his approach from other meditation techniques and describe what he shared with his patients.

In time, he adjusted that terminology again and identified his material as 'relaxing meditation'. Though inspired by Eastern ideas, Ainslie Meares' approach was distinctive and his alone, differing significantly from traditional or mystical systems of meditation. It does not involve philosophy or religious practice; nor is it intended in itself as a pathway to spiritual realisation or enlightenment. It is foremost a straightforward exercise that assists the brain's natural self-regulating mechanism to restore homeostasis, or equilibrium. In its simplicity this exercise lends itself entirely to modern Western society as a skill for self-help. It was to this refinement of Meares' ideas that I was introduced in 1974.

In his writing Dr Meares referred to his meditative style as 'the discipline of ease', a paradox in itself, illuminating in this instance the shades of effort and effortlessness required to make a whole experience. Like great or small, light or dark, black or white, good and bad — all matter and experience is of two opposites. In this case, the *effort* we require is that which disciplines us to take action to change, while the outcome of that effort is an experience of absolute *ease*. It's really that simple; we put something in and we receive something back. If we do this exercise each day, *spending a few minutes experiencing our own calm and stillness of being, in time the ease gained from the experience will flow naturally into daily life, bringing us the changes and benefits we seek.*

Ease is a normal human response — if apparently at times unattainable in our busy everyday life. And the Meares' form of meditation is typified as that — an effortless experience where the mind of the meditator is temporarily resting — in much the same natural manner that spontaneous reveries occur. By allowing this experience to take place, according to Meares, the right conditions are provided for mental regression where the brain itself is rested from the many stimuli that organ has to contend with. Here, he claimed, lay the healing necessary to relieve anxiety, tension and pain. In one paper published in the *Journal of the American Society of Psychosomatic Dentistry and Medicine* in 1978, Dr Meares distinguishes his form of meditation thus:

> There is an absence of mental activity, an absence of sensory experience and an absence of emotion. It is a regression to a very simple mode of functioning. The consequence of this experience is an absence of anxiety, and what is more important, the subject remains with a low level of anxiety for some time after the meditation has ceased, so that there is an on-flow of a low level of anxiety into the patient's daily life.

Stillness meditation today

It is said that when an idea occurs in one part of the world, through synchronism within the collective unconscious, ideas will spring up in other parts of the world by like-minded people. At the time Dr Meares was introducing his ideas to patients, others in other parts of the world were investigating similar approaches. Since then, much research has been carried out into the physical and psychological effects of meditative practice. This research includes the influences of ancient Eastern philosophies and Western spirituality throughout the ages, together with enquiries that extend as far as extrasensory perception, altered body states and the scientific observation of brain patterns. From this research, a new approach to medicine has evolved, described today as *psychoneuroimmunology*. This is the area of mind-body medicine where the mind and its related effect upon the function of the body are explored.

Recent technical research[2] in the United States demonstrates that the brain is built to respond to change and the term *neuroplasticity* describes this ability. Thus genetic inheritances can be modified. It has also been shown that while stress impairs the development of new brains cells, the practice of meditation can induce positive changes. Ainslie Meares' work pre-empted this knowledge. Without the advantage of modern technology, he had the insight, talent and passion to pursue his belief that changes in brain function could occur naturally, given the right conditions. In Meares' view, *anxiety reduction* was crucial to mental and physical health — and from that belief he developed his concept: *stillness meditation*.

Now, further to Meares' ideas, numerous styles of relaxation and meditation are accepted in our society. Any and all of these can contribute great value to people's lives. Many of these meditative approaches, however, are related to culture, philosophy or religion and this background does not suit all people. Some techniques involve complicated rules or rituals which can be confusing or time consuming. Most involve some *mental effort*. Meditators are taught *the use of a mantra or to concentrate, visualise or breathe in a particular manner, to practice mindful awareness, to listen to music, to make their mind a blank, to focus upon prayer* and so

[2] Davidson et al: Waisman Laboratory for Brain Imaging and Behaviour, University of Wisconsin-Madison-2002-2007

on. For the purpose of *meditation per se*, such techniques can be necessary and important. However, to attain *mental rest*, according to Meares, it is contradictory to the experience of *ease* to involve any effort in the process. The compelling difference between his innovative self-help skill for today's world and traditional meditation techniques, is *the simple experience of being still.*

In learning to be *still*, we may, of course, be led further to follow other enriching meditations — as a different, separate exercise; but I know, after all these years' regular practice of *simple stillness, that to successfully reduce tension and anxiety, and indeed as an adjunct to life enhancement, there is no need for anything more.* And each week I see the effect of that stillness benefiting those I teach.

In those three intervening years between the commencement of my consulting practice and Dr Meares' death, I was fortunate to have many opportunities to discuss case studies with him. His informal supervision of my work was enormously valuable to me as I further absorbed his approach. In particular I paid attention to his personal bearing as a demonstration of what he taught. Though this too was occasionally misunderstood by others, his demeanour totally exemplified what he wanted his patients to learn. When I, in the midst of agoraphobia, first met Dr Meares, my general response to life sprang from *agitation and fragility.* My immediate impression of him and his *attitude* was one which imparted a response to life based upon *calmness and strength.* Obviously he practised what he preached.

From the first moment of our meeting, I knew there was something basic I had to change within myself. Dr Meares, as teacher, exhibited his own ease to his patients, in his voice, movement and general attitude. In this way, he taught what he wanted people to learn in an immediate and subliminal fashion, demonstrating his own ease and calmness of mind, sometimes before he even knew their name. And so his patients were learning to assimilate change even before commencing his meditation therapy. His manner taught me the immense importance of *anyone's* attitude in life and even more importantly, the immense importance of attitudinal example. We learn — and we teach — by example.

Communicating stillness

In this style of meditation there is no formal instruction. Once again, the influence of example can be seen. The experience is an *experience* and only that. But the experience is enhanced by the environment and the presence of the teacher; so a prominent aspect of Meares' meditation is the communication of *ease* through touch. During the sessions Dr Meares conducted, his firm yet tranquil touch, especially on the shoulders, chest and forehead of the meditator, imparted an essential deepening of the meditation and the reassurance and support necessary for the letting go of tension.

Touch used in this way is a non-verbal message, more powerful than continued verbal instruction and devoid of any need for the meditator to keep his or her mind active by listening or concentrating. And, very helpfully, should the meditator become anxious while learning to let go, the presence of the teacher and his or her touch contributes immensely to restored confidence. But there is more than this. Since his use of verbal instruction was minimal, touch was Meares' most powerful form of communication, enabling the meditator to experience fully the state of mental stillness. His touch communicated and shared his own inner ease, a gift which when imparted to others powerfully deepened their meditation. Of course, in order to receive this gift, one had to trust.

Experiencing stillness

It is important to explain that the essence of Meares' meditative approach is this: the experience is less about learning or being taught than it is about being assisted to *experience our own stillness*. So to benefit by this means we do not *try* or *strive* or *do* anything. We learn to allow ourselves to 'be still' within an experience that transcends difficulty, discomfort, distraction or disturbance, to become one of ever-deepening calm. It can be seen, then, that while one can benefit profoundly from the presence of a teacher, essentially the stillness is there within ourselves. With this understanding, stillness may readily be achieved by following the idea and practising regularly at home.

When we avail ourselves of the experience of stillness as a regular discipline, first the body deeply relaxes, becoming heavy and still. Physical ease *always precedes* mental ease. The mind cannot come to a state of ease if the physical body remains tense. When the body is at ease, gradually our rational thought becomes suspended as our mind too, drifts at ease. Thoughts become disconnected and unimportant to us. In moments we may become aware of *un*awareness — and then of course we are aware again until that too, drifts away.

The general experience of stillness is not available to us until we leave it and return to our usual state of alertness. If we then pause to look back, we will recall quiescence and repose. . . and from that, a sense of peace, inner strength, wholeness, capability and order will flow. We will feel refreshed and energised with new positive perceptions, rather than gloom or foreboding which may have been the case before our practice. In the wake of the experience, we feel a calm control over our life and little by little we become renewed. With such rewards it can be seen that there is little need to embellish its natural process.

Even more importantly by way of definition, the experience of stillness could be likened to a daydream or reverie state which is a normal, natural and safe mental occurrence. If in our normal waking state we occasionally drift into a day-dream, we don't have to do anything to make that occur. Daydreams and their accompanying mental rest just naturally happen, almost without our knowing and often we are jolted back to reality with a start. *Stillness meditation* is something like that. Except that while daydreaming is a spontaneous, irrelevant happening, meditative stillness is a discipline, deserving of priority as a daily practice that will make life better.

Some people with faith only in fear express a fear of meditation in general, believing if they abandon themselves to meditative practice they risk the influence of evil or other negative preoccupations. Perhaps this could be a concern if one were meditating in association with cult-like involvement, or where other people can powerfully control or influence the meditator's mind. And, since I am by nature a cautious person, had I glimpsed danger of any kind or found anything but peace, my involvement with *stillness meditation* would have ended before it had begun. But the simple experience of stillness bears no reationship to exotic practices. It only brings peace, and where there is peace there is safety.

Frequently, people examine the process too closely, as I did myself at first: *Am I doing it correctly? How do I let go ... regress more? Should I make my mind relax?* These enquiries are understandable, but they get in the way of the effect. I advise people to wait, to be a little patient and answers will involuntarily arrive — or no longer matter!

Another significant aspect of stillness is that it must be experienced in a physical posture of *minor discomfort*. Some systems of meditation or relaxation advocate a *comfortable* position for the body. Dr Meares emphasised the need for slight discomfort, as *mental* ease cannot be attained *if physically we are too comfortable*. By slight discomfort, he means being seated at ease in a symmetrical posture, where the spine is erect and the body is supported by the chair and the floor beneath one's feet. In other words, physically we maintain an upright posture, at ease in repose and quite alert; but not cosy in an armchair, or slumped irregularly or lying on a bed. The purpose of the physical alertness reflects the discipline of ease and leads to a 'global' letting go: the complete relaxation of one's whole being – body, mind and spirit.

As we give in more and more to the meditative experience, without forcing ourselves in any way or trying to make it happen, the *mind learns* that it is safe and natural to be still. And as the mind becomes still, our physical sensations, discomforts, distractions and so on, gradually disappear. In the stillness, we are learning to let go beyond pain, tension, anxiety or awareness of any kind. Thus the stillness experience is somewhat like a rehearsal for our state of being in everyday life. If we are able to transcend discomfort or distraction while relaxing in stillness, then the onflow of that experience will enable us to transcend the discomforts which life may present to us.

Meeting the challenges of life

It is important that we remember, after adopting *stillness meditation* into our lives, that life *will* present further discomforts. New challenges are always arising and in these we have a choice: to view them as challenges; or to view them as potentially stressful events. While the former view will always serve us better, either way, we need to be prepared. The lesson I think, is to know that we must always care for ourself. We, as individuals, are best able to do that; no-one else can do so as well as we can ourselves. So, when challenges or stressful situations occur, not only do we maintain our regular times of stillness, but we learn to recognise that sometimes we need to increase those practice times. When pushed to our limit, we must balance that pressure with longer periods of meditative stillness.

While anxiety and the accompanying agoraphobia was for me perhaps the greatest obstacle I have yet experienced, my life has still been endowed with many potent challenges. In seeking greater personal growth or in solving various problems that have come my way, I have explored my inner life and my past life, I have read widely and investigated many theories for well-being. I have attended conferences and seminars, listened to tapes and kept my journal. I have immersed myself in one of the loves of my life — music — and I have participated in role-play and visualisation. I have attended to my soul, developing my faith and my spiritual self. All these paths I have found immensely enriching in their own right. But I return again and again from visiting the complex to simple *stillness* to maintain my ease — and in fact, to more ably reap the rewards of any and all life experience. For no matter what we *do*, the doing will be greater enhanced when it is accompanied by the wonder and mystery of the power of *being*.

Conclusion

Over my many years as a *stillness meditation* therapist I have regularly seen the profound changes also experienced by others. In reading their stories shortly, you will find that these people too, have found contentment through *stillness meditation* as their symptoms have vanished. Among these have been many sufferers of agoraphobia, panic disorder and depression, and many others seeking help for general anxiety, improved health, spiritual development or a higher quality of life. I have learned much from my clients as they share their stories with me and I thank them all for their intimacy and their trust.

People tell me how their symptoms have left their lives, how their health has improved; that they now cope with life more effectively and achieve more with greater ease. They speak of better sleep, improved concentration and increased self-confidence. They share perceptual changes

— how something is causing them worry and distress, but after stillness they can view the problem positively and with hope. They speak of their creativity flowing freely and the development of insight and intuition. They observe their life changing, renewing and improving in many, many ways. Perhaps my greatest joy in this work is to see people's fear subside, soothed away in stillness. It is vital now, to take you, the reader, on the *stillness meditation* journey, so that you too, may thrive. But before doing so, a final summary.

- Meares considered the reduction of anxiety to be paramount to good health.
- He considered *stillness* of mind to be the body's own natural way of coping with distress
- His concept of *stillness meditation* rests on his theory that the crucial factor in calming the anxious mind is *mental rest*.

Meditation as conceived by Ainslie Meares is pragmatic rather than ascetic. There is no emphasis upon esoteric or unconventional practices. As it has no link to culture, philosophy or religion this practice is suitable for all belief systems, temperaments, constitutions and age groups. A natural function of the mind, *stillness meditation* is completely safe and not constricted by detailed structure or by mental activity. Its benefits primarily result in anxiety reduction and personal composure from which general health and the serene living of each moment emerges. Though unrelated to religion, the power of this practice may present the opportunity for spiritual development. *Stillness meditation* is a simple self-help therapy for change and in fact the less it is complicated by reading about it or questioning its detail, the more effective it will be. Study of it alone is of little value. In the words of Dr Ainslie Meares, 'It is only the doing of it that counts.'

Chapter 11

CAPTURING STILLNESS

❦

In quietness and in confidence shall be your strength.

Isaiah 30:15

What I am about to describe is very subjective. Therefore my description and the experience itself is open to many nuances and interpretations by the reader. In this chapter, I will take you through three varying descriptions of the approach to *stillness meditation* in the hope that from a choice of narrative you will more easily find an understanding of what you are about to learn. This is a guide to your own practice.

But before we commence, here are several observations surrounding the practice of meditation in general:

- Meditation is not merely a crutch, as is sometimes supposed, but a vehicle for change.
- The practice of meditation does not imply inactivity, 'opting out', or laziness. Rather, it is a personal investment, providing for richer, fuller lives.
- During effective meditation certain changes take place within the body, among which the heart rate slows and blood pressure decreases. Breathing becomes almost imperceptible as the need for oxygen is lessened; and as anxiety reduces within mental rest, cortisone production decreases, opening the way for the immune system to function more effectively. So, meditation is more than relaxation, more than a technique for stress management.
- As well as assisting with emotional and physical well-being, meditation can lead to expanded consciousness and spiritual development.
- Meditation facilitates productivity and performance through the outcomes of heightened energy and clarity of mind.
- In summary, meditation provides the single most powerful means of

achieving and maintaining a high standard of well-being.
- Meditation is a completely natural means of self-help.
- Effective meditation, can, according to Meares[3], 'aid the restoration of the natural mechanisms of the mind and therefore, restore psychic equilibrium'. Modern technology now substantiates his theory as yet without the benefit of studying his specific approach.
- *Stillness meditation* is different from other forms of meditation.

When I first began teaching *stillness meditation* to others, meditation in Western culture was relatively rare. The term 'meditation' equated with something to do with Eastern Yoga philosophy or various other religious practices. These days meditation *per se* has become popular and widely recognised as advantageous for health and well-being. But there are many approaches to meditation available today. I am familiar with most and I know that not all of these *can necessarily provide what Meares taught as the right conditions for effective anxiety reduction.*

In an earlier chapter, I discussed trust and how it is often missing in the life of the anxious person. In offering this guide to *stillness meditation,* I ask now for your trust. Please trust the concept of *stillness,* its simplicity and its power. Please begin to trust yourself, and me. This natural practice can change your life.

Here is my first approach to proceeding with your practice.

Approach One

1. Physical posture

Adopting the correct physical posture is the first step and is necessary to the process of *stillness meditation.* Remember, it is not possible *to relax the mind if the body is too comfortable.* To find mental stillness, the body must be at ease, but mildly disciplined in *minor* discomfort.

To meditate effectively in this way, I find the most suitable posture is sitting erect in a straight-backed chair with the feet resting flat on the floor. The shape of the chair supports the weight of the body and allows one to give in with confidence to that support. Although sitting this way

[3] Meares, Ainslie (1963), *The Management of the Anxious Patient,* W. B. Saunders Co., Philadelphia & London.

for a prolonged time may seem a little unusual at first, this symmetrical position is a natural posture and ensures the minimum of muscle strain. With practice, one can meditate very easily in this regular and balanced position for long periods. If the chair has armrests, you can rest on them, otherwise let your hands lie separated, loosely in your lap. The head and neck are held erect — not tense, just evenly balanced. Let the shoulders drop and experience the weight of your body sinking into the chair, your feet on the floor, as you give in deeply. When seated correctly one is poised in calm control — relaxed yet disciplined, upright but at ease.

Any difficulty or discomfort in the body will pass with regular practice, and the more we practise 'letting go' within the body, the more the mind learns to 'let go' in mental relaxation. Eventually, when the mind can be still and the body becomes free of discomfort, the varying discomforts of life will be transcended in a similar manner.

Try sitting like this now and experience the naturalness of it. Don't force it, just let it happen.

2. Physical letting go is the pathway to the meditative state

In your seated posture, the next step is to recognise any tension anywhere in the body. For the first few practices, begin from the feet and work up through the body, sensing the tension and letting it release. Please don't try or force, but simply sense the tension and let go, let go, let go, giving in all the while. Particular areas of tension are the stomach muscles, the shoulders, the neck, the mouth and the jaw — and especially the face, in particular the forehead. Recognise all the tension and let it go. Relaxation will occur for a time but will be patchy. Tension will return, but don't give up. Each time you practise, allow the tension, wherever it happens to be within your body, to ease away. With practice and in time, you will become aware of tension, not just when approaching meditation but at any time throughout the day — and you will be able to let it go. After you have practised regularly in these ways for a while, you will realise that any need to physically let go of tension will be unnecessary; you will sit down to practise and physical ease will just naturally occur.

This 'letting go' should be quite effortless, without deliberate trying or striving, just letting it happen. If we try to *make* ourselves relax, the effort involved in doing so is counterproductive to what we seek.

3. Trains of thought

The mind takes longer to become *easy* than does the body. Newcomers to meditation often find it helpful to have a few words or phrases with which to get started. These are not rigid thought patterns on which to concentrate, but simply ideas or trains of thought that encourage people to give in and experience the effortlessness and ease of *being*. Such ideas are particularly helpful to highly anxious people who are afraid to relax deeply. These words or phrases within our own mind as we relax (or spoken by another by way of instruction) should continue only for a few minutes, since the whole idea of this form of meditation is never to concentrate, visualise or focus our attention or awareness upon anything. Remember, we aim to experience only *our own inner stillness*. As you practise, use words in your mind (self-talk) if you need to, just to commence and until the mind eventually loses interest in pursuing them. The inner words or thoughts used should be positive but without stimulus, encouraging your mind to be infused only with **a sense of your own ease**. For example, one might allow the following words to surround the experience: 'effortlessness', 'easy and natural', 'a good feeling', 'drifting deeply', 'letting go', 'more and more', 'really wonderful'.

In your posture, let your eyes close now; sense the release of physical tension and allow your mind to accept some of those trains of thought. Don't try in any way, just *experience* the ease of it all.

4. Stillness of mind

Now, ever so gradually, those ideas will fade, become distant and unimportant to your conscious mind. Thoughts lose their logical or critical content and become barely distinguishable, washing over your consciousness like the ebb and flow of the tide. Sometimes on the journey to stillness of mind, certain images, colour patterns or dream-like experiences may occur. These distractions are of no concern and will pass as you learn to let the mind relax more and more. Noises, discomfort and other distractions fade into the background to assume unimportance. The whole self is very still, and you remain in that meditative state, knowing only the ease of yourself for as little or as long as you wish...

When ready, just slowly open your eyes, rest for a short while and then, refreshed, resume your day's activities. And that's it: *stillness meditation* – a self-help therapy and the art of doing absolutely nothing.

The four steps outlined above to help you proceed are really one effortless experience. The process of this kind of meditation is not a series of steps to be mastered, so don't become involved in trying to perfect your posture, physical relaxation, trains of thought and stillness as four separate exercises. Each factor is important, but *stillness meditation* is not divisible in this way. Remember that it is rather like a daydream state; simply give yourself wholly to it in favourable circumstances and in time, stillness will occur quite naturally.

Approach Two

Here is another way to approach practice. While *stillness meditation* is really the experience of *doing nothing*, we reach that experience of *be-ing* by accepting an element of *do-ing*, summarised in the following five steps:

Desire
Commitment
Environment
Posture
Practice

✺ Desire

As we move towards participation in anything, the first requirement is *desire*. To *desire* is to wish for something. Within our heart we wish perhaps for *relaxation, peace of mind, improved health, freedom from fear or for general well-being*. Or maybe for *a life focus, better relationships or spiritual growth*. Whatever our wish, it is prompted by a desire for something to *change*, for something to be *different*. Desire, then, is a motivating force — an action, the *do-ing* of something. It moves us closer to our goal. And so our *desire* for stillness is the first step in attaining this as part of our life experience.

There is a practical advantage in desiring *stillness meditation*. From a matter-of-fact position, this practice of stillness is surely the least complicated, the most portable and the most easily and naturally accomplished. We don't need to be in a particularly special place or wear special clothing. We don't need to have a tape player at hand. We don't have to remember individual words, nor do we have to spend energy in creating or maintaining visual images. We don't have to *depend* upon anything. And once we have learned and integrated the exercise into our daily life, we don't even have to have a teacher.

And we don't have to bring anything to the experience of stillness — but our heartfelt desire for it — and *commitment*.

❧ Commitment

Successful participation in anything requires *commitment*. Commitment to anything we pursue will always bring positive results.

When we commit ourselves to our *desire*, we access the tool that really inflames our enthusiasm and brings the reward of achievement. And while *stillness meditation* is not about *achieving* as in 'doing', nevertheless it is a life experience which will not occur without our commitment to its taking place. Commitment stands at the threshold of all hope, promise and purpose. Through commitment we state responsibility for ourself and our desire for change — from which will spring the satisfaction we long for.

Stillness meditation is a beautiful experience, therefore it is deserving of a beautiful *environment*.

❧ Environment

Since beauty is always in the eye of the beholder, there is no universal environmental requirement for the meditative practice. We simply create the opportunity of a space in which to meditate that brings joy to our heart.

As beginners, we will most likely seek our stillness in a restful room, perhaps where the sun comes in through the glass on a winter's day. Or we may wish to meditate in an environment that accents our special treasures — family photographs, a classic sculpture, a sacred icon, books, a favourite armchair, seashells, flowers, crystals or candles — *our personal things of beauty.*

A beautiful environment may be a secluded place in the garden where the stillness is discovered beyond fresh air, the gentle breeze or our remote awareness of the movements, scents and sounds of nature. Or by water, the flow of which can set the scene for tranquillity.

For beginners, quietness is important to the meditative environment. So is soft light and freedom from the distraction of such things as the phone or fax or miscellaneous technology. Later, when we have become more proficient meditators, it is possible to experience our own stillness within the hustle and bustle of modern life — in fact, in any environment at all.

❧ Posture

In the meanwhile, we learn correct meditative *posture*. The purpose of *stillness meditation* is to *relax the mind.* We can only experience that under the right circumstances. Therefore the *ease* of our body is a prelude to the ease of our mind and occurs as follows:

We sit symmetrically in a chair, not *too* comfortably, just in minor discomfort and so that we remain poised and alert. In this posture we have a sense of *control* which, paradoxically (in a kind of effortless self-discipline of our entire being) leads to the giving in of total relaxation. Our body is erect, balanced. Our feet are flat on the floor, our arms resting in our lap, or on the arms of the chair. We are completely balanced, poised and at ease. Quite effortlessly.

❧ Practice

In this posture of ease, when we are ready, we *let* our eyes close. We make no effort. We *let* our eyes close, and, *giving in,* we let our *practice* take place. Remember, to practise stillness is to *just be* . . . We are not going to *make* ourself relax in any way. To try to do so would completely contradict the experience. For *stillness meditation* is an experience of *not trying.*

Poised and at ease, we hardly notice our physical body — but as a beginner, learning this simple practice, it may be helpful to observe tension anywhere throughout our being, and *gently let it go.* To 'let go' may be challenging at first — especially if we are particularly tense. (Tension, of course, is an habitual and negative way of keeping control. In fact, tension, rather than availing us of control, propels us *out of control*.) So, to experience *ease*, we learn to let the tension go.

The face, in particular, is a reflection of our inner tension. In practice, we allow a smoothing out of the muscles of our face — noting the tongue, the jaw, around the eyes and especially our forehead, and we let it all go, *just being e a s y* . . . Poised and at ease, we sense the ease in our face, radiating throughout our head and flowing down and down to the very centre of our being... in stillness...

Our WHOLE being, easy and natural, gradually becomes a unified being of stillness. We sense it — and we give a little more, letting ourself BE more and more completely. There is no effort. No technique. No need to try in any way, or do anything. As we sit in this way, we know only stillness. *And 'the mind learns'* something new, different, calm and still. *And so we remain, for a time embraced in a state of whole relaxation, body, mind and spirit at peace, and at one.*

After a little time like this, when we are ready, we allow our eyes to open slowly as we return to the present. Then we rest quietly before resuming our daily activities. A short transitional rest is important. Remember physical changes will have occurred as our body slowed down. The body now requires time to readjust.

Approach Three

Here is a third descriptive passage, taking you in another way, into the *stillness* experience.

You sit in an upright position, disciplined but at ease, just slightly uncomfortably.
Your feet are flat on the floor,
your hands are resting loosely in your lap.
You allow your eyes to close,

you allow your shoulders to drop a little.
You sense what it's like to let the tension go a little;
this is a taste of what is to come.

You may feel some resistance to letting go.
You may feel slightly afraid, but
let go a little more.
Observe your entire body.
Observe its resistance.
Perhaps you notice yourself gripping inwardly,
or you may notice the gripping of tension in your shoulders, throat,
face or jaw.
Allow all this gripping to ease away, gently, little by little.
It will grip, you let go.
It will grip again . . . you let go again.
Observe other parts of your body:
where are you gripping?

Notice how the gripping occurs again and again, quite habitually and
spontaneously.
Remind yourself that this has been your 'normal' response to life for some
time.
Remind yourself that you can let this go:
it will take time and repetition —
but you *can* let go.

Observe your face, especially your face.
The face expresses the emotions within.
Observe your whole being and the way you return to old habits . . .
holding on, steeling yourself, fighting something as yet unidentified.
This response is within you, but it's not your natural response — it's a
defence you've learned.
What you now seek is *naturalness* –
the way you once were, the way you really *are*,
Beyond, beyond the fears conjured up by imagination.

In this moment, now, let go a little more throughout your whole physical being.

If I were with you, I would be speaking gently,
and now I would let my hands rest on your shoulders,
gently communicating the ease of your whole being.
Suppose you could sense my touch here and now and
experience this encouragement...
my touch is light, expressing everything I want to tell you:
that it's safe to let go; that you can do it; that, in letting go,
inner stillness will come to you and you will be restored to peace and
strength.

You sense that touch on your forehead, smoothing away the stress of
many days, months or years.
Let go into that touch and sense its message.
At this moment you are like a child who is distressed, now being comforted and reassured.
It's safe to languish in this reassurance,
it's safe to let go.

You sense the touch fall gently away, taking with it all your strain.
You are distantly aware of quiet words of reassurance.
You let that awareness go,
and the words become more and more distant, less frequent,
until they too, disappear and there is stillness.
In the stillness you may feel afraid again.
Let the fear fall away;
move beyond its illusion,
The reality is within you, your own strength, naturalness
and truth.

You stay a while in this stillness.
It's a good feeling.
You let go into it more and more and more completely, and

you sense something wonderful, a temporary journey into something new.
Your conscious mind may register this newness with alarm,
may try to warn you of risk or danger,
may pull you up with a start.

There is nothing to fear,
just old habits, testing you.
You let go again and allow the stillness in once more.
Your body is at ease,
your mind is at ease,
Beyond distraction or disturbance to the silence and stillness of *simply being*.

Just being. Naturalness.
Effortlessness.
And you stay with this awhile,
just letting . . . not trying, just letting yourself . . . simply be.

Yes, there may be thoughts,
there may be itches or distracting sounds from outside –
but you let yourself go beyond these.

And you sense the peace.
Trust yourself and allow it to come to you,

simply being still . . .
And, having remained in that safe place for a time, when you're ready, allow your eyes to open ... very slowly ... and rest quietly for a while.

Now that you have these specific guidelines to practice with, there are probably some questions or other considerations to address. I believe the following will cover most of these.

Summary of key aspects

Before listing the likely questions, I offer the following summary of key aspects to *Stillness Meditation Therapy.*

Qualities and Benefits
* a simple solution
* a natural practice
* a life-enhancing skill forever where:
     calmness replaces agitation
     anxiety decreases
     tension lessens
     symptoms gradually disappear
     post meditative calm flows into general living
     wider benefits emerge as a stable life is restored.

Difficulties for anxious minds
* the anxious mind has long been programmed to retain control
  – this may present difficulties at first because, in stillness, the anxious mind must learn to let go
* anxious people may therefore feel more afraid for a time and may be tempted to give up.

Please remain on course by
* accepting the discipline required
* being courageous and committed to change
* maintaining trust
* seeking encouragement or assistance
* preserving patience
* persevering, regardless
* repeating your *practice, practice, practice.*

Questions and answers

What do I feel when meditating?

At a much later date and after regular daily practice has been established, a profound sense of ease and well-being is experienced. One feels very little, apart from an inner knowledge of being untroubled, within an all-pervading comfort, certainty and the security of peace. It is not really possible to specify how one feels, since the meditation experience is unique to each. When your meditation session has ended, in retrospect you will know that stillness was captured and a state of rest was sustained.

What am I supposed to think about?

You're not supposed to think about anything. This is an experience of physical and mental *rest*. Bear in mind that if you are focusing, directing your thoughts, noting your awareness and so on, your mind is not resting. In *stillness meditation* you are simply *allowing* your complete self to be still. With practice, thoughts will separate and recede, becoming more dream-like and less logical. The mind will never be completely 'blank' but between those separated thoughts, calm, undisturbed stillness will be experienced.

Where and when should I meditate and for how long?

Once the practice is established, one may meditate at any time and in any place, at will. Most people meditate best in a familiar place and usually somewhere private. But to meditate out of doors is a beautiful thing to do. Experiment as the quality of your meditation improves. It is wise to set a pattern for practice from the start and it should, as a minimum, be practised for ten to twenty minutes twice a day. One can meditate for longer periods and can, if necessary, get by on a little less. It's a good idea to meditate first thing in the morning before the day is in full swing and again in the evening, preferably not too late at night.

Many business people and other professionals find that fifteen minutes' practice in the middle of their working day brings welcome and beneficial respite. So don't become tied to time. The most important thing is to meditate *some* time.

Some people are distracted during meditation by a concern that they will go on for too long and be late for work and so on. If this is a worry, use a timer for a while, but soon you will find the body-clock giving a satisfactory reminder that it is time to end the session. Above all, meditation should be treated as *the most important event of each day.*

How soon will I see results?

In my experience, you should see significant benefits within a couple of months of regular practice. The achievement of deep stillness takes time, so remain constant in your application of it. Likewise, full freedom from specific problems can take up to two years of regular sessions and practice. However! From the onset of your dedication to this meditative state, *changes will begin to take place.* So the sooner you commence, the sooner you will feel relief.

In the case of severe anxiety conditions such as agoraphobia, remember that these have become habitual responses which may have existed for a long time. Therefore there is much undoing and re-learning before confidence is fully restored. But as long as you are practising stillness, you will begin to feel better just the same.

For these conditions, I suggest practice sessions lasting one hour, several times a week, over and above regular practice times. The longer the session, the greater the quality and therapeutic value. When practised in this way, stillness is more powerful and the results will be hastened. Remember too, that as individuals we will respond to this individually. Eventually the results will be apparent. After all, what is a couple of years of gradual improvement compared with five, eight, twelve or more years of anxiety?

There is a parallel to the recommendation of increased practice time for higher anxiety levels within Dr Meares' work with cancer patients. When he observed that profound and prolonged stillness in meditation may have a positive influence in arresting the progress of certain life-threatening illnesses, he emphasised that people using meditation under those circumstances must devote much longer periods of time to its practice each day, at least in the critical stages of illness. It makes sense therefore that the higher the anxiety, the more times of stillness will be needed until things improve.

What should I do to avoid interruptions to my practice?

The best way to ensure twenty minutes' peace is to warn those around you that this is your time and you do not wish to be disturbed. This is perfectly reasonable. Switch the phone off or learn to ignore it for that time and only cease your meditation if there is no alternative. It's a good idea to slot your practice time into a part of your day where the likelihood of disturbance is minimal.

How can I overcome a tendency to fall asleep during meditation?

Some people tend to become drowsy during their session. This often occurs during an evening session after a day's activity and is generated by normal fatigue. Those who become drowsy, I find, are people who can *physically* relax very easily. While sleep is not the aim of the meditative experience, this state is not that of normal sleep and the meditator still gains, regardless. When I first began practising as a teacher, I held classes in a church hall. The only available chairs were quite hard and uncomfortable. Yet some people fell asleep! I discussed this with Dr Meares at the time, and he was impressed that these sleepy people were relaxing deeply enough to go beyond the discomfort of those chairs. The positive changes to their well-being soon proved that their drowsy state was not sleep, but very deep mental rest. In experiencing *stillness meditation*, ideally the mind is clear, calm and still. Once again, this will come with practice and the passing of time.

However, some people become annoyed by the drowsy state. The best way to prevent its occurrence is by increasing the discomfort a little more.Increased alertness can be maintained by keeping the posture more erect, using an even harder chair or stool, keeping cooler or temporarily making the mental decision to aim to stay awake. Meditation is best practised early in the day, anyway, when one is fresh; so if you are simply too tired, abandon meditation at that time; go to bed and truly sleep instead.

What do you think of alternative or advanced postures?

I don't think they are particularly necessary. However, as you become more confident and proficient in meditation, you may experiment with a variety of postures. But it is unwise to flit from one to another too frequently at first. Lying flat on the floor can be useful if you are extremely tense, or if through illness you are unable to withstand sitting for any length of time. Lying flat is a very 'giving' posture, particularly with the palms of the hands open. But lying flat (even on a hard surface) can sometimes become too physically comfortable and therefore not conducive to relaxation of the mind in the meditative state.

Kneeling is challenging and takes practice — it is not for beginners. Sitting on the floor cross-legged suits some very well, and is a versatile posture for use in spontaneous situations, such as out of doors. You can also try using a high-backed armchair and resting your head on the back of the chair. This is an alternative that is good for beginners, but at times it can cause muscle strain or conversely, can be too comfortable. As pointed out earlier, never hope to achieve mental rest while lying on a bed or curled up in a cosy armchair. *Stillness meditation* cannot take place under those circumstances, because the comfort of such situations comes only from physical relaxation and not from the function of the mind.

Do you think there are some people who just can't meditate?
This obstacle is rare and usually due to an extraordinary fear of letting go — in all probability caused by early life issues involving physical, sexual or emotional abuse. The individual has become 'programmed' to hold on in every way, due to long-term need of extreme self-protection. With good guidance, such people ultimately do very well in meditation.

I was meditating quite well and began to feel faint and ill. Why do you think this happened?
This can be partly due to physical and mental adjustments to the new experience of letting go as opposed to holding on. But also, a co-incidental combination of lowered blood pressure together with a drop in blood sugar can be a contributing factor. This may be a simple 'vasovagal' incident but usually, when questioned, people admit to not having eaten for some hours! A glass of water and some barley sugar is the short solution. Eating good food regularly is even better.

Why is one meditation session really deep and at other times nothing seems to happen at all?
Learning to meditate is like learning any new art or skill and one must expect fluctuations in progress. Yes, one session may be excellent and the next apparently not so good. That is normal and will eventually stabilise but nevertheless benefits are still forthcoming.

Other considerations

Perseverance is necessary
Some people can move into the meditative state quite readily and see results quickly. Our gifts differ, and what comes naturally to one may not do so for another. But all who persevere with meditation will benefit, of that there is little doubt.

As mentioned earlier, within a month or so of frequent meditation sessions with Dr Meares, I was aware of a significant improvement to my state of fear. But it still took me a good twelve months of regular sessions and regular practice to be really free of agoraphobia. For some it may take less time, for others much longer. As we are individuals, so we will individually progress — providing we persevere.

The less restriction the better
As beginners, the less restricted we are in any way the better we can relax. When you approach your meditation session, it's advisable to remove heavy glasses or jewellery and to loosen any tight clothing. Undo your belt and slip off your shoes. When learning this skill, the freer we are, the better. Later, when the meditative state is readily achieved, freedom from restricting garments is less important, providing, in fact, a discomfort to learn to relax beyond.

Stillness flowing into everyday life

I am sure you now understand that the objective of the practice of stillness is that of a better life. The exercise in itself is a special encounter, but it doesn't end there. The stillness then flows on into all we are and all we do. You can enhance this occurrence by bringing stillness and ease to your awareness from time to time throughout the day; by deliberately releasing tension whenever you feel it, and by carrying the tranquillity of the meditative state into your every response. In these ways, we truly live with ease.

A general word

As stated before, experiencing a state of stillness will not usually occur readily at first. In fact, this may not happen for quite a long time. Though the exercise in itself is easy, it can take up to two years of regular practice to reach deep and fulfilling *stillness meditation* — and then the rest of one's life to maintain it! But be consoled: as stated above, the power of the experience will have a positive effect on your life right from the time you begin.

At first, there will be many distractions in the form of aches and pains and a stiff neck, or back or muscles in general. There may be boredom, irritation or despair. Itches will become evident for no apparent reason and the desire to cough or to sneeze may tempt you. There will also be tension and there may even be mild panic or other unwelcome sensations. But please stay with it. Your body is learning something new; your *mind* is learning something new. It may take some weeks of regular practice before you even feel relaxed in any way at all. So when you feel frustrated, don't be too concerned; the next day's practice will be different — and probably more successful.

Through daily meditation, in due course you will begin to feel at least physically relaxed and may start to enjoy the time. There may be small signs of general ease in daily activity, where before perhaps, life was almost always difficult. As physical relaxation develops, the mind begins to relax as well. At first, stillness of mind is elusive. Remember that in everyday life the mind is never still; even in sleep it is busy caring for your body and expressing your innermost self through dreams. So we cannot expect the mind to come to a state of ease immediately.

When meditation is first attempted, the mind produces lots of wonderful ideas to keep it occupied. Never before has thought been so active! Our worries surface; we remember what we should have remembered before; a song repeats and repeats itself like an old recording, stuck in the groove; the traffic in the street outside seems incredibly loud and we wish someone would do something about the racket those birds are making. People frequently become despondent, judging their progress harshly: 'My mind will never be still.'

Please be reassured. This is a gentle discipline, so we need to employ a little *practice, patience and perseverance*. In time, the activity of the mind *will* diminish. Intermittently, moments of calm will occur. At another time, or perhaps on another day, more calm descends and thoughts are less intrusive, until eventually in exquisite stillness, nothing disturbs us at all. And yet you will always be in control, because it is always possible to cease the session immediately, whenever you wish to do so.

Practice is for ever

It was my habit, long after I had overcome agoraphobia, to continue to attend sessions with Dr Meares occasionally, simply for the extra pleasure and benefit they afforded. *Stillness meditation* is a procedure to be first established and then well maintained. Where it is not possible to attend classes with a proficient teacher, the practice of *stillness meditation* must be regular to ensure ongoing benefits. It is unwise to find success by this means and then become so casual that old habits of tension arise and anxiety builds once more. It is not uncommon for people to stop practising stillness once their symptoms disappear. People believe they no longer need it, as life becomes easier and more inviting. But predictably, stressors will arise and without the benefit of ongoing stillness, symptoms of stress, tension and anxiety may manifest again. So give stillness the priority it deserves. We all know how important it is to prioritise dental care? I believe mental care, looking after our mind, could be even more important than our teeth!

Stillness in each day is a lifetime commitment for those who wish to live well; but a very pleasant one. Our practice of stillness provides a special opportunity, a time of quintessential rest for the whole being. Yet this is also a growing, living art and therefore each meditative experience is as unique as the meditator. It is a beautiful experience. Do it, and enjoy it. And within it will come a certain knowledge that all is well.

Chapter 12

CONQUERING FEAR

❦

The world is too much with us; late and soon,
Getting and spending, we lay waste our powers:
Little we see in Nature that is ours;
We have given our hearts away, a sordid boon!

Wordsworth

In Part One I have told my story and discussed at length the symptoms and the experience of living with agoraphobia. But agoraphobia is only one manifestation of anxiety and tension — albeit a severe one. At grass roots, any phobia, obsessional reaction or anxiety disorder originates in our personal level of anxiety and tension. Please understand that the practice of *stillness meditation* is effective for any anxiety condition or destructive emotion — including depression. The integration of that practice can change your life, no matter what symptoms you may be experiencing.

In addressing the effectiveness of *stillness meditation* and in guiding you towards your own daily practice, I have given you what I regard as the golden key to the door of freedom from fear. At the risk of repetition, from hereon I would like to share some additional ideas and practical suggestions which may also be supportive to the reader in overcoming fear in general. For once the door has been unlocked, to discover what lies beyond the threshold one must take practical steps forward. But before we proceed, please remember that no matter how your anxiety manifests, it is unlikely to lessen or leave you until you have satisfactorily reduced it *and* your tension level and begun to respond to your life calmly as one does when practising stillness. You must attend to this first.

Tenets to follow

Only you can do it

If we wish to improve our life, only we ourselves can make that happen. We can learn from others and be assisted in our progress, but the first step to change and the will to succeed in what we desire is each person's responsibility. We must also have the ambition to become independent again. If we are too well supported, it is easy not to try. As anxiety 'disorders' are well recognised today, this relieves some associated embarrassment. However, it would be inadvisable to adopt the attitude: 'Lots of people have this kind of fear, so I don't really have to change; and I'm used to it anyway.' This is definitely not aiming high enough. You are worth far more than that.

Blind acceptance is not of much help either. Acceptance of the problem for what it is will be the right attitude — but not without understanding — and never to the point of resignation. And keep perseverance at a premium to allow time for positive change to stabilise.

Discard the label

Acceptance of the existence of anxiety in life is realistic. But to accept a specific label for oneself according to that anxiety is rather like accepting an indictment of personal limitation. Today, people are categorised as having an anxiety disorder such as social phobia, agoraphobia or obsessive compulsive disorder; such categorisation may be diagnostically useful to the clinician, but rarely helpful to individuals. If you have been given such a label, heed it for purposes of understanding and then let it go. Detach yourself from it, as to a sensitive, anxious person, this fuels susceptibility to negative suggestion and therefore increases anxiety. You don't need to complicate your fear with other issues.

Incidentally, this subject matter points out the necessity for anxious people to take steps to positively develop their self-image rather than reinforce existing insecurities. Ignore the label and carry with you instead the affirming thought that you are a beautiful human being — who is sometimes insecure.

It is easier to overcome a problem when
we understand it more fully

Most people who fall victim to fear do so because anxiety and their own natural defence against it has not been properly explained to them. I hope my story has made this a little clearer. Lack of understanding or incorrect understanding increases people's vulnerability so they feel more readily threatened. The fear-filled person defends him/herself by increasing tension and avoiding whatever is feared. Avoidance becomes habitual and, just as in agoraphobia, the body becomes trained to react whenever a similar situation is presented. Each recurring occasion brings about more defence and therefore more tension; so the victim becomes trapped on that not-so-merry-go-round described throughout this book. In understanding this pattern you will be empowered calmly to take control of your situation.

Know and believe that you are not alone in fear

It is very natural for human beings to feel afraid. It is comforting to know that all people experience fear of some kind at some time in their lives. As you continue your journey, observe others in theirs, and with compassion observe their vulnerabilities; theirs will not necessarily be the same as yours, but they will exist just the same. Be encouraged by what you see and consider sharing your story with a trusted friend. The stories within this text are a demonstration of people's courage in their pain. You, too, have an abundance of courage with which to achieve a happier and easier life.

Know and believe that
the symptoms you dread will not hurt you

Assuming that you have no illness to cause similar symptoms (and you will have been reassured of that by your doctor), accept those symptoms for what they are and you will dread them less. No matter how long those unpleasant feelings have peppered your life, or how greatly they alarm you, you have been deceived by a flimsy illusion: fear feeding on fear. That is all.

Tension is the reason for compelling fear

In seeking to conquer your fear you will have explored many different forms of treatment. I hope these have brought you comfort and help. But if fear is remaining as master of your life, you are still carrying a high level of tension in your body and in your mind. Watch yourself and you will certainly discover that your usual way of living involves holding yourself tightly, bracing yourself to face the day, fighting from within to maintain control. The anxious person usually seeks relief from symptoms or panic in the following ways: *swallowing a tranquilliser or retreating from the situation*. From having read this book, you should now know that the opposite reaction — the way of tranquillity — is the way to harmony, health and happiness. Here are two examples that substantiate my argument.

In the first instance, symptoms will be temporarily averted because of the lowering of tension due to the effect of the drug. But as soon as this effect has worn off, the cycle repeats itself and you are back to where you were. In this case, you either become dependent upon medication or continue to feel discomfort —neither of which is a satisfactory solution. In the second example, the act of retreating from the situation to safety brings a flood of relief. It's not the fact that you have reached your car or arrived home that stops panic, but the letting go of tension that accompanies the relief you feel at reaching safety. Unfortunately, until tranquillity is personally integrated, this tension release will only be temporary. Therefore it is of paramount importance to become a naturally relaxed person. Then, and only then, will you become the master and fear the servant.

Learn to breathe correctly

Long before I experienced high anxiety, I had learned diaphragmatic breathing as a student of singing. In the midst of my mounting tension and anxiety, somewhere, somehow, my breathing technique got lost. Re-learning this technique came readily to me once I regained my confidence, and it was some years before I realised that the vast majority of people have never been exposed to the concept of correct breath control. It is very important for *anyone* to breathe correctly and I particularly recommend this to anyone who is anxious.

One of the major reasons we first panic is the unfortunate experience of hyperventilation, which occurs from fast, shallow chest breathing. When you can manage your breath well, you reduce the possibility of panic while at the same time caring for the well-being of your body. Correct breathing is natural breathing. Find a baby, observe him or her breathing as they sleep and copy what they do. You too, breathed naturally at that age. If you can't change your breathing without more assistance, seek a reliable source from whom you can learn and integrate diaphragmatic breathing.

Move through panic, not away from it

A panic attack always follows the same pattern, featuring some or all of the following sensations: the stab of fear and pounding heart, giddiness or unsteadiness, sweating palms, nausea, breathlessness, hyperventilation, visual disturbances, weakness or faintness, palpitations, 'pins and needles' or numbness in the extremities of the body, feelings of unreality, confusion, a sense of being overwhelmed by something unidentifiable and a general feeling of terror, with the urge to escape the situation.

Calmness and tranquillity prevent panic from occurring; therefore the practice of stillness will provide you with the antidote to anxiety. It is not possible to be *anxious and calm at the same time*. However, should you feel this state of tension rising, you must let go into it and allow it to pass. Remember, fighting it or running from it in terror involves an increase in tension which will in turn increase anxiety, prolong the attack and eventuate in full-blown panic. Every time you take that action, you reinforce an existing habit. Every time you act in the opposite way you reinforce a new, tranquil response. This will enable you to truly face your fear.

Habits, when recognised, can successfully be overcome

To the phobic or obsessive person, this point may seem to be an impossibility. This is not necessarily so. At some stage of life, tension has been learned as a 'normal' coping mechanism and it has become an automatic response — a habit. Now you can make a decision to try another approach — relaxation — and make that a habit. Tension brings no happiness; the opposite can bring much happiness. Phobic or obsessive reactions are habits in themselves, where people automatically practise avoidance or compulsions to allay their anxiety. These are defence strategies, based upon past experience. The past is over; stay in the present. In this way, you can cease being burdened by two negative habits working against you.

The following example, familiar to the agoraphobic, will explain what I want to say. Occasionally, when all excuses have failed, the anxious person may be in a situation where an engagement or appointment must be faced. He or she is absolutely cornered, and short of breaking a leg in the next fifteen minutes (a choice many might prefer!), will be on the way to the dreaded place. Once there, he or she will feel some relief and a release of tension, reassured that having got this far with no harm yet (although on the alert for it) he or she will survive the occasion.

As anticipation of the event is always more fearful than the event itself, the sufferer may even begin to relax a little more — but only temporarily. Ultimately, habitual tension will creep back and anxiety will rise, bringing with it potential discomfort, and symptoms of panic. Note that when relaxed a little the fear temporarily abates until the familiar attitude of tension intervenes. What now has to be learned is the reverse, making *relaxation* the familiar (or normal) attitude. Very simply, the bad habit has to be broken.

Let go of habitual worry

Constant worry, another expression of anxiety, gets us nowhere. We all face from time to time matters that cause us concern. Regardless of the worry that may preoccupy us, problems resolve themselves eventually and usually our worrying had no influence upon that resolution. Worry complicates issues when our energies would be better spent in seeking positive proactive solutions and developing the power of optimism.

Like tension and other negative coping strategies, worry, a response learned from somewhere in early life, becomes habitual. Among other things, people who are fearful are often also inclined to worry unnecessarily about the 'why' of their condition. Gaining self-awareness through an understanding of our beginnings and our life path is a valuable growth process. But searching for the specific cause of one's anxiety can become a fruitless and introspective preoccupation which often increases anxiety further. If you faithfully address the matter of tension in your life, worries will diminish.

Laugh and have fun!

It has long been said that laughter is the best medicine. To live without laughter, nonsense and fun now and then is to take life far too seriously. I have a special friend with whom I share laughter and fun. I treasure her friendship and look forward immensely to the times when we get together. Her ability to find humour even within very testing situations (and she has known many of these), is her special gift and perhaps her greatest strength.

Make sure you invite laughter into your life by seeking friends who can laugh and have fun, by watching films or reading books that make you smile, by looking for opportunities to see the bright side or the funny side of incidents within your day. Giggling is good for you! And find occasions that call you and those around you to rejoice and celebrate. Bring fun into your life and fear will be replaced with elation as your spirit soars.

Waste no more time

Since the breaking of old habits largely constitutes the overcoming of your fear, do not delay any longer; begin now. Observe the tension in your physical being as you read this. You will notice it in many places — particularly in the muscles of the face, forehead and jaw. You do not need to be so tense. Practise letting it go. Let go like this continually as part of your life. It must become habitual to let go of tension, just as in the past it has become habitual to hold on to it. Constant awareness of this will assist you to break that vicious circle of which I keep reminding you. Practise letting go at home, in the car, as you're walking or working — anywhere. Release your tendency to brace yourself or fight from within; go with it all instead. When anxiety symptoms appear, go with them — and let them go. Do the same with thoughts that plague you; attend to them and they will hover, dismiss them and they won't recur. Here are a few examples to keep in mind.

A woman who has suffered from agoraphobia for some years told me that her main pastime is gardening. She loves her garden. However, she prefers to work at the back of her home, as whenever she spends time in the front garden her neighbour stops to chat. I quote her: 'I feel so trapped. It's not so bad if I'm near the fence, because if those anxious, unsteady feelings begin the fence is there for support. But I dread having to talk to her without something to hold on to.'

In this story the woman is without fear until she feels restricted by her neighbour's presence. Her symptoms are telling her how little control she has in her relationship with her neighbour. However, that is not the point of this anecdote. She anticipates the scenario and is already prepared, tense. As her symptoms begin to rise, she is then afraid that she will panic and collapse and make a fool of herself — so she instinctively increases her tension to fight this possibility, making the likelihood of an unfortunate outcome far more probable. In trying to defend herself from embarrassment, this person has developed the constant *habit* of tension — and increasing tension. She must learn to go with, not against, the symptoms at (or before) their onset and then she will be free to enjoy the company of her neighbour without apprehension and fear.

From my own experience, I recollect a turmoil of anticipation of fear due to a particular dinner engagement. Some people who live with what is known as social phobia are daunted at the prospect of socialising. That was not my fear, but I was always afraid that panic might occur in such a situation, and of what the end result would be. On that occasion when we were seated and as the hostess served me, I felt overcome by a sense of weakness and began to feel panicky. Because I had no wish to offend my hostess, I remember thinking as I picked up my cutlery: 'I must at least make a start.' This I did, eventually enjoying the entire evening. Had I known then what I learned later, I believe it was 'making a start' which relieved the tension.

If faced with that today, I would first physically relax, that is, let go of all apparent tension within my body. Then calmly make a start on whatever situation I was facing, and then, in the same calm and easy manner, go through with it. While all this positive action is taking place, tension is released and panic will not strike.

Someone else told me of an occasion when, after much worry and build-up of fear of leaving the house, she eventually drove to a meeting. By this time she was late and the meeting had already begun. The symptoms of fear rose up as she approached the door and the infamous invisible brick wall came up before her. All she could do was retreat to her car in panic and drive home again, thoroughly mortified. Had she been aware of her tension level and had the courage to let the tension go as she walked to that door, I doubt if the wall of fear would have occurred. She would instead have gone calmly through the door to the meeting, and her symptoms of fear would have abated and no longer troubled her.

The aim, as in each of these cases, is always to let go and move beyond the symptoms to achieve one's goal. This is the pattern which, when repeated and repeated, breaks the habit, breaks the vicious circle and gradually restores confidence. It is with this *life attitude* and by these means that all exaggerated and recurring symptoms of fear will be eliminated from your life. Keep experimenting. With anything that daunts you, let go. With every triumph over tension, no matter how small, your confidence will increase until suddenly you are fulfilling your life in ways you didn't dream possible.

A lesson

You have successfully reduced your anxiety and symptoms have left you. You are happily moving on with your life and bang! There it is again! Do not be surprised if occasionally symptoms seem to appear again. Remember, it is normal to experience anxiety, especially in times of stress. These symptoms are your way of expressing anxiety, therefore they are of value to you. Others may express their anxiety in physical illness and their illness will move them to take a holiday, get more rest, resign from their job, etc. Now is the time to ask yourself: what is the message that my expression of anxiety is giving me? Am I too tired? Is my relationship not compatible? Do I need a holiday? *Have I abandoned my practice of stillness?*

Any or all of these factors plus a thousand more can be reason for the temporary reappearance of symptoms. These are merely little echoes of an old melody, a part of your life that has made you who you are today. Please do not be alarmed. Should symptoms reappear, that does not mean that you are slipping back to where you were. You never *can* do that; you are a different person in a different place now, richer and wiser for it all — and you have the skills to prevent that happening. What you can learn from this, though, is that self-care is of vital importance for all your life, especially the care you give yourself in meditative rest. What you can also learn is that anxiety is a messenger, serving a purpose. Heed its message and know that anxiety can never hold you in awe again.

Ten positive ideas to read and re-read

1. Each day set aside time to practise *stillness meditation* as I have described. Do not try to fit it in to unsuitable times or rush the exercise. It is impossible to achieve any kind of ease if you know the vegetables are going to boil dry, or that you should have left for work five minutes ago. Remember, recognising physical tension and developing the habit of letting it go is the pathway to mental rest. And it is the regular and deliberate introduction of times of effective stillness that provide the right conditions for the most favorable mental rest.

2. Cultivate an attitude of ease in your everyday life. This will stem from the practice of *stillness meditation*, but in overcoming your fear you need to bear it in mind until it is the way you live.

3. Have the courage to say to yourself when you feel anxiety or panic symptoms arising: 'I am tense. If I let the tension go, the feeling will pass. If I hold on to the tension, the feeling will increase and persist. The more I practise letting go, the less I will experience symptoms — and the less afraid I will be.' If you adopt this attitude, you can feel the tension and fear drain away.

4. Let go into your fear. To force and fight against it only stimulates the body's reaction to fear. and that is what you are trying to stop. No matter what situation you are facing, think: 'I will do this and I will do it calmly and easily, letting go of tension all the while.' There is a vast difference between forcing yourself to do something and simply doing something with a sense of ease. Keep in mind that you are easing your anxiety, not trying to control it.

5. Stay in the present moment! Every time you begin to recall former situations where you were afraid, let those memories go. People

paralyse themselves even more into avoidance by recalling all the other times they have felt afraid or failed to accomplish something. Those memories keep fear alive and well. Keep your focus upon success *now*, challenging yourself gently to move on. With every success, no matter how small, there is a pleasant recollection to dwell upon, making the next time easier still. And remember — others around you are scared too!

6. Keep going towards your purpose. Every time you retreat in fear rather than relaxing, letting go and calmly making the distance, you feel you have failed again – and so your memory stores failure as a familiar outcome. But, in the same way, the repetition of good things leads to familiarity where success becomes the outcome. Like learning and practicing anything, the more we do it, the better and the *easier* it becomes. Then we have success and feel triumphant – and confidence grows even more.

7. Learn to cultivate a positive attitude throughout your whole life. For happiness, positive thinking should be the automatic response. Negativity and the pessimism it produces are powerful, but, once a positive attitude becomes automatic, optimism will dominate. Take every opportunity to make the positive work for you. If confronted with a long queue, rather than considering its disadvantages, remind yourself that this is an opportunity to relax and release tension. When stationary at a red traffic light, rather than continuing to grip the steering wheel, use the time to relax your whole body. When disappointment occurs, rather than viewing it as a catastrophe, look for the advantage it may bring in other ways. *Read books on positive attitudes!*

8. As soon as you feel remotely ready to meet a challenge, go for it! But approach it with that same attitude of calm and ease. Creative interests and absorbing hobbies, particularly when enjoyed among other people, are invaluable as distractions to place unreasonable anxiety where it belongs — in the background. You might have an ambition to begin a new career, or to commence a course of study you once dreamed of. Meet the challenge, and as you go from strength to strength, your life will become fuller and fear will be long forgotten.

9. Never give up; the worst is over. Even if you have lived with high anxiety for a long time and a future without it seems beyond contemplation, you will soon prove it otherwise.
10. Remember! It is the constant awareness of the tension within us that is the green light to freedom.

Chapter 13

CONQUERING AGORAPHOBIA IN PARTICULAR

Keep off your thoughts from things that are past and done;
For thinking of the past wakes regret and pain.
Keep off your thoughts from thinking what will happen;
To think of the future fills one with dismay.

From a Chinese Poem: Po Chü-I, AD 826

Over the years, I have learned that the agoraphobic person has many questions he or she needs suitably answered. Most likely my own story has filled in many blanks and I will discuss in the following pages further symptoms. In seeking ways to help yourself, I will also offer some additional ideas for your consideration, addressing matters that may be specific to agoraphobia. But first, here are, in my opinion, the three major rules:

Three rules to follow

1. Take responsibility for changing your situation.
2. Learn and practise *stillness meditation*.
3. Face your fear through regular challenge.

Since these steps require substantial action on your part, the question may then be asked: 'If it is so necessary to make this much effort to overcome my fear, how can sitting still in meditation help me?'

Here is the contradiction, for once we accept that change is our own responsibility and begin to practise stillness, the calming occurs without our trying or making any effort at all and fear becomes easy to face. Metaphorically, as long as we chase the butterfly in the garden it will continue to elude us — but if we sit quietly and wait it is likely to land on our shoulder.

Of course, none of the following ideas will necessarily be appealing to or suitable for all people. Nor will they necessarily have an effect. However, they have contributed to my own success story and many others have found inspiration or motivation from them. You may find suggestions here which individually, or in combination, may be helpful at times when progress seems to halt or waver. In any case, these suggestions are all based upon positive action and practicality: it is always beneficial to do something towards change. Doing *something* — anything — will almost always dispel anxiety, whereas avoidance will reinforce it. For while the discovered 'ease of being' will open the door to freedom, we still must proceed to what lies beyond.

If you are severely handicapped by agoraphobia, you may not want to try these ideas at all. I know how great your fear and resistance can be. I understand how little confidence you possess and how greatly you rely upon others. But remember that no matter how severe your anxiety, or how many years you have been affected by this condition, you can still attempt to regain at least a partially 'normal' life. The process has to be gradual, because you are un-learning a learned reaction. Be positive and believe that you will succeed, for when we doubt, we falter. Progress may be very slow at first but that is the best way, slow and sure; for each person will overcome fear at his or her own pace and in his or her own time. *Most importantly, you must learn to become very relaxed.* Please study the meditation instructions in Chapter 11 and put them into practice ! This will reduce your anxiety making each day easier.

I recall one woman in particular who had been housebound with her 'full-blown' phobia for some thirty or more years. She was very anxious, dependent upon a great deal of medication and very nervous about attempting *stillness meditation.* A relative accompanied her each time she attended, and after a number of sessions she relaxed a little. Soon she was coping far better than before. She even *looked* less afraid. She found she could remain at home alone and could now go to certain places and enjoy occasions, in the company of her relative, that she hadn't faced at all for a long time.

The need for mental rest

Before I proceed, I want to say again that *without being calm and easy in ourselves* no alternatives are likely to prove completely or permanently effective in banishing agoraphobia. That is my firm belief. The mental rest experienced in *stillness meditation* is the means by which ease is attained naturally, while reducing the level of tension and anxiety at the same time, and I quote from *The Wealth Within* by Dr Meares:

> In the case of a severe fever, we need rest. In the case of a fracture, it is a matter of immobilising the fragments of bone in their correct position. In the case of anxiety, it is a matter of allowing the mind to come to a state of quiet and stillness.

So mental rest is a must, leading to a calming and enriching way of life. Then, when we are calmer, we can make a start on other things, letting go of tension all the time and slowly confidence will be restored. In a manner similar to the development of physical fitness, the more we do the more we can do. We accumulate coping ability as we accumulate physical strength, extending ourselves more and more in a relaxed manner until the goal is achieved.

Aspects of anxiety: a review

Some specific aspects of anxiety that can accompany agoraphobia may need to be reviewed at this point:

- The symptoms of anxiety usually prompt people to fear that there really is some 'other illness' causing them. Once you have sought adequate medical advice for reassurance, unless you are dissatisfied with the service you receive, don't run from doctor to doctor searching for new opinions.
- I have touched on the effect of obsessive thoughts or actions previously. These are a misguided attempt to manage anxiety. Thus these annoying reactions can also become part of the agoraphobic person's life. Like other symptoms, they will pass when you become wholly relaxed, but you can help them on their way by coming face

to face with them. Take time regularly after each meditation session to contemplate why these obsessions are necessary. What purpose are they serving for you? Ask yourself what would be the worst thing that could happen should you dare to oppose your obsession. Question their presence in your life. By doing this, you will come to understand when and why the obsession began, probably many years ago. From quiet contemplation you will more readily see that this response is no longer a necessity in your life. With the gaining of insight, try while very relaxed to face the obsession and break it. Even to attempt this will be a very small step at first. But with continued application, these symptoms can successfully be put behind you.

- Monday mornings often greet the agoraphobia sufferer with intense anxiety. Some people find that their fear diminishes noticeably when they are out of their routine and in the safe company of others at home. Weekends are wonderful! But when the coming week dawns, everyone else goes off for the day and the victim of agoraphobia is left to his or her own resources, feeling immensely troubled once more. Or the reverse can occur — routine suits some more than others, and at weekends these individuals fall apart. These reactions will vanish once *stillness meditation* takes over from anxiety.

- Depression, as mentioned before, is another common accompaniment to agoraphobia — and understandably, too. If the depression is severe, you need medical help and possibly medication for a time. But like other symptoms, it too will pass as stillness reduces the overall anxiety level. In some instances, as recovery occurs agoraphobia will pass but depression will replace it. This seems to indicate that a significant emotional issue is emerging and often expert counselling or therapy is needed — in tandem with meditation practice — to seek and resolve the problem.

- Lack of concentration is a frequent symptom of high anxiety and is commonly present with agoraphobia. And I know there is also a fear or resistance to reading books concerning the symptoms discussed here. These tendencies make it difficult to absorb helpful material — but they won't stop you meditating!

- I have discussed susceptibility to negative suggestion briefly among the suggestions section of Chapter 11. Further to that, it is imperative that agoraphobia sufferers watch 'self-talk' for habitual negative suggestions. A collection of positive statements should be amassed to counteract negative self-talk. They must, however, always be statements of one's own. In other words, they must reflect your own want or need, and not simply be the repetition of an idea produced by someone else. Spend time when very relaxed quietly discovering what you need to do to counteract negativity in your life. In doing this, you will come to know yourself much better, and find eventually that for the most part you are producing your own pain.
- When people are extremely tense and anxious they are usually highly sensitive to noise, light, traffic or temperature. Domestic machines will seem to vibrate beyond tolerance, and people feel the heating system is set too high, the clink of a spoon may cause a minor physical shock, or, feeling scrutinised, they may ask themselves: 'Why is she looking at me like that?'

As already noted, the agoraphobic can also experience severe headaches, difficulty in swallowing, breathing problems, insomnia, fatigue, doubts as to one's sanity and an inability to cope with life. Like the others, these symptoms will disappear when the mind becomes rested.

In Chapter 4, we looked at ways to overcome fear in general. All those suggestions apply to agoraphobia. The considerations presented now will expand upon what has already been said and perhaps be helpful to your general well-being.

Additional considerations for the agoraphobic person

Medication
If *medication* has been prescribed, it is wise to take it as directed until *meditation* begins to take effect and the need for sedation is no longer apparent. It is not sensible to remain dependent upon drugs indefinitely. When taken this way, these chemicals can produce symptoms like those of anxiety, and of course drug dependence can lead to the possibility of

addiction and its unrelenting consequences. However, neither is it sensible to disregard the advice of your doctor. And in times of great stress it is quite appropriate to make use of medication — but only now and then and in the short term. For medication is never a cure, only a crutch; the problem with a crutch is that the more one uses it, the more one needs it. The wise person will aim higher than that.

One must also remember that because anxiety and tension are in themselves a natural response, they will, unless otherwise reduced, always override the medication; this means that the amount of medication taken is continually being increased to counteract symptoms — another good argument for the natural reduction of anxiety and tension. If you have relied upon medication for some time and you wish to discontinue it, do not attempt to reduce it without medical supervision or without the support of organisations dealing specifically with this process.

'Recreational' drugs

In the same way that prescribed medication can create anxiety symptoms, many people have developed agoraphobia following an experience of panic while smoking marijuana or using other powerful drugs. Be warned and avoid this destructive influence on your body and your mind.

Diet

Diet is important to everyone. Excesses of caffeine, alcohol or cigarettes are understood to increase anxiety. Too much sugar or junk food is known to be detrimental to good health. All the literature on health today emphasises the need for the right foods and the right vitamin supplements and so on.

Many health professionals today agree that certain foods can cause a sensitivity reaction in some people. Such a reaction is a form of stress in itself and *may* aggravate the anxiety condition. Whenever the body experiences stress of any kind, there is an instinctive fighting response which manifests in tension. This can be experienced by some in generalised feelings of physical tension, or as a more direct physical response such as an awareness of the heartbeat, shortness of breath and an overall sensation of being 'hyped up'.

In looking at the problems of stress, anxiety, tension, panic and agoraphobia, we are looking at individuals who have reached their current position through accumulated stress and tension over a long period of time. Therefore it is important, in decreasing this accumulation of stress, to consider the multi-factorial aspects of the problem and reduce as many stress factors as possible by appropriate means to bring full recovery. In this respect, it may be necessary for some people to also change their diet.

This is not to say that food sensitivity or intolerance alone causes panic or agoraphobia. Nor will diet alone affect the general anxiety and tension level. However, if there is a food problem which a change of diet can eliminate, then there is one less form of stress for the body to deal with, one less potential source of tension, one less set of symptoms to fuel anxiety and therefore, one less negative factor to contribute to the whole anxiety pattern. Seek advice from your family doctor, a dietitian or from a natural health practitioner.

Hormonal activity

Women, who are said to be the major sufferers of agoraphobia, often identify greater restriction by way of anxiety in the days preceding menstruation. Hormonal changes during pregnancy and premenstrual tension are widely recognised today as a form of stress for the body to contend with. It is understandable, therefore, that tension and anxiety will be higher at these times. PMT, together with the influence of fatigue, from time to time can be contributing factors to the agoraphobic condition. It is wise at such times to take extra care of your body.

The benefits of physical exercise

Physical exercise is an excellent way to dissipate tension and anxiety, and of course is beneficial in other ways. Seek exercise that suits you and determine to pursue it. Don't fall into the trap of allowing agoraphobia to prevent you from doing this. If you are really determined, you will find the ability to 'get there' — talk your support person into joining you in this! Walking is the easiest, least expensive and most natural of all. Take courage, start with small distances and build upon this gradually. Swimming is excellent. Yoga is ideal, where you can also learn to breathe correctly and complement the use of *stillness meditation*. Massage, though not a form of exercise, is a luxury which can ease tense muscles. And if all else fails try dancing to the radio or running on the spot!

Together with the fear of being away from home, some agoraphobia sufferers fear physical damage through exertion. Actually, your awareness of your heart and other physical discomforts are more likely to be your body protesting from *lack* of exertion. Seek your doctor's advice and with his or her blessing — though it may take time to build up fitness — do make a start on this. The practice of stillness after exercising is a lovely thing to do and as your body gains stamina, so will your mind gain ease.

Developing your spirituality

For fullness of life, it is important for all people to develop their spiritual self. Spirituality means different things to different people. Those with faith in God will relegate their lives to His power, love and mercy. Others will find consolation in the natural world. Take time to reflect upon your commitment to spiritual growth and to sense where your needs and beliefs are centred. If religious practice is part of your life, draw deeply upon its gifts. Read and search widely all great spiritual, mystical, philosophical and literary writings for inspiration and action. In seeking meaning, understanding, self-control, greater tolerance and compassion, the inspiration you may have overlooked in your own scripture may be discovered elsewhere and so your faith will be strengthened and your life enriched. Psalm 46:9, 'Be still and know that I am God', is comforting. Likewise: 'I will always be with you; I will never abandon you. Be determined and confident' (Joshua 1:5-6).

From among the sayings of the Buddha[4] , here is something to consider:

> Why do I remain thus in constant fear and apprehension? Let me bend down to my will that panic, fear and horror, just as I am, and just as it has come to be. So as I was walking to and fro that panic, fear and horror came upon me. Then I neither stood still nor sat

[4] Woodward, F, L, (Tr) 1925-1960 *Some Sayings of the Buddha*, Oxford University Press.

> nor lay down, but just walking up and down I bent to my will that
> panic, fear and horror.

If you have no overt spiritual leanings at all, you might consider the the absolute wonder of the universe as inspiration in your search for inner wisdom and peace.

Join a support group

Support groups can be helpful. If possible, be part of one. Humorists joke about support groups for agoraphobics, because for obvious reasons there is rarely anyone in attendance! But rest assured that when you are there you are with others with the same fear. This increases confidence and builds courage. Even the fact that you can *sometimes* attend support group gatherings will aid your freedom from fear.

Sharing the problem in these groups and the strength gained from knowing one is not alone in fear means that support groups for agoraphobia sufferers are valuable. Loneliness is lessened, people become open and wholehearted and bonds of friendship and contact are formed. Whether agoraphobia improves as a direct result of support group contact alone is doubtful, but at least company makes the condition a little easier to bear. And the elusive element of 'togetherness' in such groups can also provide some compensation for much of the closeness lost through isolation. However, support groups should aim to be constructive, not just another means of dwelling upon the problem.

In recent years, agoraphobia clinics have become established in most cities. These can prove beneficial, particularly from the point of view of finding reassurance, taking positive action and discovering ongoing support.

Sharing your fear

Much earlier I discussed the advantages (or disadvantages) of sharing your fear with friends. As you gain confidence by sharing your difficulty in a group, you may feel ready to seek encouragement from others. Anyone you trust can be your source of encouragement; but someone who inspires you will have a greater effect. Discuss your difficulty with a trusted friend or professional counsellor. And surprisingly, wisdom can often be found right at hand, not necessarily from professionals but often from those with a wealth of life experience.

Driving
If you enjoy driving a car but have resisted doing so for some time, build your confidence again by asking your support person to drive his or her car ahead so that you travel in tandem. In this way you won't lose sight of your support, but you *are* driving alone. This is best tackled first on short, familiar trips and gradually extended to more exciting places.

Steps towards personal fulfilment
Lack of personal fulfilment is a major contributing factor to agoraphobia. By this I mean the development of 'personal identity' through achievement in the work we do in the market place or at home. Many who are agoraphobic have not found satisfaction in their work, nor do they balance that lack of fulfilment with satisfying activities in their leisure time. It is important to seek what one needs in life to feel fulfilled and to take steps towards achieving that. At first those steps may be tentative, but they are of great significance, nevertheless. We don't *have* to live a life of compromise. We are meant to seek happiness. Set your goal and gradually move towards it. Agoraphobia will retreat as you go forward.

Creative activity
Creative arts are highly therapeutic and may lead in time to greater fulfilment. Any of the many forms of music may be one of the best art forms in this instance, because music provides companionship even when one is alone. Music is beneficial too because it is very disciplined, and discipline (with ease!) leads to order in one's life. Gradually set about finding a way to involve yourself in your preferred field of creative activity. Some teachers will come to your own home, an excellent way to begin this part of your journey.

Helping others
When more relaxed and as soon as is possible, take steps to do something for someone else. Join a fund-raising committee. Volunteer to keep

someone company or give of your talents to help others. As you become to a certain extent a support person to another, you will find that your own fear is likely to recede. When we give out, in due course we receive. Do not, however, see it as your obligation to live at the beck and call of others — a situation which may provoke anxiety via the covert negative emotions of guilt, resentment and anger.

Finding self-awareness

Many sufferers of agoraphobia lack self-awareness, self-esteem, self-confidence, self-assertion, self-acceptance, self-love. Educate yourself further by reading relevant books and, where possible, attend courses and seminars to help you understand yourself, your reactions and your interaction with others. But a million books and seminars will be useless unless you put into practice at least a little of what is learned from them.

In seeking self-awareness, a good way to do this is to buy an exercise book and keep a journal to confide in. If one writes down what is on one's mind — about any issue, large or small — thoughts become clearer. Sadly, because of modern technological communication, the days are gone when we would pour out our heart in a long, handwritten letter. But we can keep a journal, just for our own use, and thus retrieve some of our own *feelings*. Rarely, we will discover, are we feeling what we *think* we are feeling. From the written word, insight into ourselves is often revealed. It is particularly important that this work be done by hand, thus involving the creative side of the brain. Painting or drawing as a means of self-expression are also highly recommended.

Setting goals

As you set about recovering from agoraphobia, don't attempt to follow a structured regimen. This can be overwhelming. Instead, keep things simple and natural. It is useful, however, to set yourself realistic daily goals and attempt some achievement each day — again, always when relaxed and with a positive belief in your ability to succeed. If agoraphobia is not too restricting and you already cope with many things without too many limitations, it is not so difficult to widen your goal horizons. If agoraphobia is very restricting, try to achieve *any* positive advance (even within the home) that is beyond your usual scope of activity. Positive actions are cumulative. And they make you feel good too! Eventually the day will come when the front gate will not be so threatening and indeed, in time, the world itself will open to receive you.

Keep it simple

Simple things are usually the best. You have very likely tried many remedies for agoraphobia and most have probably not helped very much. Some theories are very intense, some are complicated and others are less orthodox — such as the person who was recommended to smash her kitchen crockery to vent her feelings and then sit down and patiently restore it all with glue. As a strategy for alleviating agoraphobia this was unlikely to be effective!

Because of the influence of modern medicine and technology, we generally believe that the best in life must be either expensive or complicated. That is not necessarily so. Simplicity is part of our naturalness, so it must be good. Believe this, and adopt the meditative stillness I have validated.

A final word

As already indicated elsewhere, some people make fast progress to recovery and notice very quickly the difference that stillness makes to their lives. Others take much longer. Be patient and persevering. There are usually a great many ups and downs, and commonly much turbulence, before liberation is complete and a 'normal' life is resumed. (Please note again that your meditation practice should be applied with particular diligence if under extra stress, or when one feels temporarily overwhelmed.)

Do not be tempted to think that you have to be in any way exceptional to reap the rewards of *stillness meditation*. A great many people have successfully benefited from this form of meditation and doubtless for many different reasons. If I did not believe others could also find relief, I would not have dedicated so much of my life to promoting it. Trust the stillness and heed my support of it. But more than anything else, try it, for it is only by *doing* it that its benefits can be known.

Earlier, I noted that symptoms can recur and that there is always a lesson for us in this. As life becomes more inviting, anxiety may be present at times. To prevent this happening, one would have to reject everyday events and opportunities and take no responsibility for one's life or potential. In other words, one would have to remain a child. But that is to opt out. It is also boring, for we exist in order to grow. Our very existence is imperfect too, and the fact that anxiety is present sometimes only indicates a stepping stone to further fulfilment. With the practice of stillness, we can move firmly from that stepping stone to the next stage of development. *And while ever we rest our mind, anxiety can never overwhelm us as it has done in the past.* One flows with it all and 'it' passes, a ripple on the water.

So if at times you seem to go backwards a little, remember that this is only temporary, like a crack in a healing wound. When things go wrong, keep an optimistic attitude, knowing that for some reason it was meant to happen this way. Good always comes from bad, in due course. When you wake each morning, give thanks for this day with the promise it holds. Recall regularly, with interest and affection, all the events and those people who have touched your life, knowing that each has made their contribution to you, forming you to be the person you are now. Look forward to all that is still to come. And each evening, as you drift into sleep, gently bring to mind at least one good moment from the day that's just passed. That keeps hope alive.

Chapter 14

TO THOSE WHO LEND THEIR SUPPORT
❦

But the waiting time, my brothers,
Is the hardest time of all.

Sarah Doudney

One of the most generous acts offered to another is the act of selfless support given by spouses, partners, families and friends of the person with agoraphobia. To give out in this way requires either absolute dedication to the person concerned or absolute duty in the face of this constraining influence. There are few ready rewards for supporters. And the mystery accompanying this dis-ease, its apparent fickleness and its accumulating frustrations can put great strain on any relationship. Yet there is usually someone in the life of the anxious person who can be there for those who need them, a fact that could be said to be astonishing given the apparent absence of care at times visible within our world. Those who continue to support and assist prove the truth that love appears in many guises and as always, will triumph regardless.

The thoughts in this small chapter are especially for those of you who lend your steadfast support to the person who needs you — a tribute to your dedication. If you, the support person, have read this book for the benefit of your wife, husband, partner or friend, I thank you. I hope my own story, my experience in this field and the contributions of others will help clarify any aspects of the problem which you did not fully understand. You need to be clear about this problem as much for your own sake as that of the anxious person. For he or she, in suffering the symptoms of fear, has been affected by these to the extent that fear dominates their own life, and consequently, the lives of those around them.

Your presence

In your support you are indirectly being asked to give much. At the top of the list of giving there is a need for your presence and for that presence to be consistent and reliable. There is a need for your untiring patience when so often you reach exasperation point. You are required to impart, time and again, many forms of comfort and reassurance, day or night. You are required to be encouraging, when at times you feel you are wasting your breath. You must be helpful when for most of the time you feel quite helpless. Great flexibility is required of you as plans may change without warning. Your faithfulness is required, demonstrating your love, compassion and commitment to the other person. And in all this you are required to remain calm and strong yourself. To meet the expectations of qualities such as these may at times seem impossible. And yet, in your support, you achieve this. And that is an admirable presentation of love.

The symptoms of anxiety are overwhelming in their grip. They are a genuine experience for the person you care about and they override reason. Fear, maintained by tension, perpetuates the consistent symptoms of physical illness which lead to insecurity and avoidance. But, as can be seen within my story, this situation can be corrected when the sufferer learns to relax, moves forward calmly and develops self-confidence. Until this renewal takes place, your potent assistance will continue to be needed.

Your co-operation

Apart from the ongoing need for your physical presence, your reassurance is of enormous aid to the anxious person. He or she needs to know that you will continue to care, despite the intrusion of anxiety. The person who experiences acute anxiety, panic attacks or agoraphobia is generally not an ordinarily fearful or weak person. Although there may be some exceptions to this, you probably know already their characteristic tenacity and the capacity this person possesses in his or her personal strength, giftedness and capability. Your re-confirmation of these qualities will help increase lacking confidence. Added to this, helping the anxious person let go of any limiting diagnostic label associated with their difficulty can be another form of positive reassurance. Again: he or she *is not an agora-phobic* but is a valuable human being — who is experiencing a form of vulnerability.

If your partner's anxiety has amplified to the level of agoraphobia and their life and yours have been turned upside down for many years, it may seem that in some ways I am over-simplifying the problem. But as he or she begins to take calm control and unwarranted fear diminishes, the essence of the battle will become crystal clear and its simplicity will be recognised. In the meantime, however, the constraints this situation puts upon your relationship cannot be rectified until the tension and anxiety levels have lowered, so a little more patience on your part is required.

The unpredictable nature of anxiety can create tensions of another kind within relationships or within the home. In the case of the agoraphobic, when safely within the household or in some other friendly environment, he or she may no longer seem to react with need. A certain self-reliance and freedom in this comfortable space seems to take over. But in a matter of minutes, just when you imagined you could readily pursue something of importance within your own life, should a threatening circumstance arise, capricious fear will be aroused and the agoraphobic will need your assistance yet again. So your own life is, in many ways, just as precarious as the life of the anxious person. It is therefore helpful and important that you keep your own anxiety and tension levels to a minimum.

Tension, as I have said before, is contagious. If you too can learn and practise tranquillity, especially through meditative stillness, this can only be of benefit to all concerned. In participating this way and extending your support to embrace the possibility of making changes in your own life, you are offering a superior form of encouragement. To ensure positive progress and a return to composure for the person you support it is also very important that you enthusiastically encourage him or her in their own reduction of anxiety. It is crucial to their change that they obtain mental rest, if possible from the regular practice of stillness as explained in this book. You can also bring your support to any of my additional suggestions for overcoming fear as outlined in earlier chapters.

Your attitude

To those who are tempted to be impatient with the sufferer or to make accusations of hypochondria or of their being neurotic, please try to understand their predicament. All people have 'neurotic' idiosyncrasies. It may be helpful for you to recall your own experiences of alarm or worry concerning your well-being. By putting yourself in the position of the other, you may be more able to recognise, at least to some degree, their discomfort.

Perhaps you are afraid of spiders, or maybe you cannot tolerate heights and you have tailored your own defences to meet these situations. Your partner or friend is also trying to defend him/herself from a specific fear, something larger than life which seems constantly to threaten. And as well as the apparently spontaneous symptoms, he or she is being pulled in two emotional directions — the way of reason and the way of emotional fear. This conflict in itself escalates confusion, together with more anxiety and tension.

The anxiety sufferer, as earlier discussed, experiences guilt within this condition. He or she is all too aware of the negative influence of anxiety upon the family or the relationship. In much the same way as an illness will affect normal living, certain concessions may have to be made and certain limits may have to be accepted for a time. But you — and the rest of the family — though you may be foregoing some privileges, are surely not being unduly deprived. In the meantime everyone will manage and eventually order will be restored. Within these circumstances, you, the support person, may be best able to appease unnecessary guilt and demonstrate your continuing acceptance of your partner and the existing problem, whilst still encouraging change.

Communication

You are no doubt the anxious person's sole confidant. You are honoured with his or her absolute trust. And he or she is extremely dependent upon you and your trust. Therefore, at the present time, you are almost a sustaining power to this person. It is really important that you cultivate maximum communication between you, so that you both know where you stand. Express your own frustrations, listen to those of the other person and learn to truly share feelings. You may consider seeking professional counsel as a partnership to assist in these areas. In communicating well, you both may discover areas of your life together where practical changes could bring relief which may also relieve part of the power of anxiety. And you may also discover needs of your own which your partner, though anxious, may be happy to assist with. Or there may be other factors surrounding your relationship to which the supported person can positively contribute by way of compensation for all you do in his or her times of need.

In your enthusiasm, please refrain from shallow advice such as 'pull yourself together' or 'get yourself a job'. Anxiety, panic and agoraphobia will not disappear simply through logical intervention or external distractions as some people suggest. Anxiety sufferers can sustain catastrophes such as the illness and death of a child yet still remain agoraphobic. However, the aim for fulfilment in life and the continual striving to be free from fear are in themselves powerful motivators to be approved of at all times.

It is possible that once the currently restricting fear is no longer preventing your partner or friend from accomplishing the task of living, you may begin to feel threat, disappointment or even anxiety. Life has been certain the way you have known it. Suddenly it is different. The one you love is no longer depending upon your presence, but is experiencing facets of life that you have no part of. This is excellent progress for him or her because it indicates deeper change through their developing security and self-awareness. But you may really have preferred things the way they were. This is when it is imperative to talk, communicate and know each other. This is the time to acknowledge that life is comprised of spiralling growth experiences which peak and plummet, but when fully lived, lead ultimately to the good of all. Those who shield themselves from the fullness of life with all its highs and lows, and those who never learn, adapt, adjust or change can be the less for this. As one grows, so the other will be affected and have also the opportunity to grow. So when your partner finds freedom, please try not to resent this fresh independence. Some adjustments *may* have to be made between you, for once freedom is regained, there will be no holding this person back as they return to living in a manner which the rest of us take so easily for granted.

To those beyond the intimacy of the support person, those outside the family circle, I would note that the majority of people who develop anxiety conditions are not looking for attention or pity; nor do people in fear wish to be patronised. What is needed is reassurance, guidance and, above all, a clear understanding by themselves and others of the nature of their emotional predicament.

The anxiety sufferer rarely experiences panic after the first attack. It is the fear of *possible* panic that causes dread, avoidance and eventual agoraphobia. But people in this situation may become agitated by their fear when alone or in a public place. Although most will fight the feelings and cope without assistance, sometimes someone in distress may seek help from a member of the public.

One woman recalled an incident where she became panicky while in a large department store. She knew very well that her discomfort was that of anxiety — the symptoms of fear — and her only desire was to escape from the store, away from the crowded and restricting location. Those who came to her aid were, of course, concerned that her discomfort was something of a more serious medical nature and insisted upon taking her to the store physician. He was not immediately available and so her feelings of impending panic were increased as she was expected to wait for the doctor. All she wanted was a rapid return to home and safety. The managerial staff in this instance had a duty which they performed admirably. But unfortunately their care was not of very much help to the misery of the ongoing fear of the woman concerned.

The lesson to be learned from this story teaches the rudiments of overcoming anxiety: rest, reassurance, reassessment and subsequent renewal. When these are engaged, panic is prevented and so the problem of distress of this nature is unlikely to arise. But the public should know that when a distressed person expresses a wish to 'get out of' a situation, it is more likely that he or she is feeling panic than the effects of some major illness.

Probably the best advice to anyone who might encounter a person who is temporarily incapacitated by fear, is to take *his or her* advice and add to it their own serene reassurance that all will be well. If the distress passes when the person is calmly escorted to a place where he or she feels comfortable, then those who have come to give aid can be sure that they have taken the right approach by helping in this way.

The person who is fighting feelings of fear needs to hear 'Don't worry, I understand. The way you feel is caused by fear and fear is real and common to all human beings at some time in life. Relax, let go . . . be calm and the fear will leave you.'

When we move to reassure a distressed child, we use gentle touch and gentle words. Really, it is the same for all of us . . .

PART THREE

And Others Say...

Chapter 15

SUCCESS STORIES
❦

**Success nourished them; they seemed to be able
and so they were able.**

Virgil

The anecdotes of others who have made their way successfully through
anxiety could be likened to lamps burning in the darkness to light the
path and lessen the journey.

Storytelling is an important form of sharing that can reassure, guide
and assist as we grapple with the inevitability of our personal passages.
Here is a potpourri of others' stories, the contributions of a selection of
the people who have travelled with me since the first publication of this
book. While some are more self-revealing and more complete than others, each story is a microcosm of individual lives and reflects memories,
thoughts, ideals and triumphs. Above all, each tells of calamity being
transformed primarily by *stillness* into personal growth and change.

Gillian

I was frozen with fear and just didn't know what was happening to
me. Was I going crazy? Was I about to die? My heart was racing so
fast and my mental state made everything familiar seem unreal and
unreachable as though I wasn't a part of it. Various things had happened to bring stress into my life and then all of a sudden the panic
attacks began daily, and then several times a day until there seemed
to be no respite from them. The symptoms were there from the
minute I awoke and through the night I would wake with the same
dread and more physical symptoms. I was physically and mentally
exhausted and my whole world was shrinking. Living, as I used to
do without thinking about it, began to get more and more difficult –
driving my car, going to the supermarket, going out anywhere, being

alone – all these normal things became impossible. I couldn't even walk to the letterbox without panic and feelings of faintness and dizziness. Noises were so amplified that even watching TV was a stressor. I didn't understand what was happening and no one else around me seemed to understand what it was like for me. Over about 6 months I had many kinds of treatment. Medication didn't agree with me, in fact taking medication made my condition worse. Then I had a dreadful four week stint in hospital where behavioural therapy was the main source of treatment offered. Despite other difficulties, returning home was welcomed.

Pauline, in a desperate and depressed state I saw something about your meditation classes and I knew I had to try this. It was my last hope as nothing else had worked for me and I was continually getting worse. In making an appointment I didn't think I would ever get there because at that stage I wasn't really leaving the house. With the help of my then partner, I remember walking through your door so distraught – desperate for help but in a complete state of panic – to the point of being incapacitated. He had driven of course, and the only way I could attempt to travel in those days was by lying down across the back seat of the car. I also remember that when I actually got inside your rooms I was clinging to my partner and begging him not to leave me. I think it took some time and some gentle persuasion on your part for me to let him go and even then, the consultation was conducted with me lying on the floor! I was **so** ill – and insecure and terrified – though it was such a relief that somebody really understood what I was going through. I wanted to believe that this was going to help but I still thought I might be the 'one' that couldn't be helped. I had a lot of doubt as at first I couldn't sit still for five minutes, let alone an hour! Then it was very hard going to those first group meditation sessions but as I continued to attend, slowly something started to change inside me. I practiced the meditation daily at home as well as attending classes and gradually began to notice I would have times, even though short at first, where I would feel at ease with myself and everything around me.

I started to be able to do small things that I thought would never be possible such as driving short distances and attending to 'normal' day to day duties. As the weeks progressed, these calm times extended for longer periods and as the months passed the hope I had, grew. This wasn't a short process but it was slow and steady – and it has been a lasting one. I am so grateful for it. I've realised it is possible to change but *stillness* must be practiced regularly.

Now, as I look back to that terrible time before, I can see that I've come such a long way. I have raised two teenagers on my own, I have survived the death of my father and the months of grief surrounding it, I have been able to initiate separation from my partner after recognising that it was an unsatisfactory relationship, and I have been able to live normally, naturally enjoying life for a number of years. Recovering from agoraphobia was a bumpy road at times. But I know there will always be challenges in life and I now have the calmness to cope. Really, I've found myself … and that's all that matters. I hope this story will help someone else.

Douglas

Here is a recollection which might inspire the reader by the richness of a life, its vulnerability and strength and its limitations and liberations. Fear or anxiety can especially be seen here as a path to travel, not as an end in itself.

Douglas, an Englishman, was born in 1926 to a military family. In his early life, the family moved around the UK following his father's career, which also included a two-year stint in Malta. His father was discharged from the army for health reasons and Douglas has early memories of hard times during the Great Depression. He also recalls his secure home life and immense love for both his parents (with a special admiration for his father), his painful shyness as a child, causing an utter aversion to school attendance and the avoidance of social interaction with his peers. An early rise in tension occurred at his mother's reprimands when he didn't 'join in'. Discovering the countryside and a life's desire to live close to nature became powerfully implanted within him as a source of joy. Some disruption to his peace occurred, however, after the birth of his younger sister, when his mother's new requirements of him created a barrier in the closeness of their relationship.

An incident at school where Douglas was blamed and punished on behalf of others taught him 'not the difference between right and wrong but the significance of justice'. Then followed his failure to pass an examination for Grammar School and the opportunity to attend Technical College to study engineering — but no opportunity to study art, a passion in early life and a gift only finally expressed in more recent years.

With the outbreak of the Second World War, 'life took a different direction'. His father was called back to service, and though Douglas was miserable and ill from missing his presence at home, he pushed himself to 'get a Saturday job and begin to study aviation'. Seeking an escape from college (which reproduced a way of life still greatly disliked), he began finding excitement and respite from visiting airfields and bombed villages nearby. This led to a search within the services for a future and to Army Apprentice School. Though the thought of war both 'excited and saddened me', Douglas found happiness and success along this path. He was recommended for officer training, volunteered for India and was commissioned into his father's regiment.

The practically non-existent social life in India was of no consequence to Douglas, but he found it increasingly hard to cope with the purpose of being in India at all. A sense of monotony, of being 'shut up' without variety, and the British approach to the Indian Raj created feelings of conflict — he was there to fight for a cause, but 'my inner feelings were for Indians to be allowed their own destiny'. He described his feelings at the time as 'full of anxiety'.

'For a change of routine I decided to give the Officers' Mess a miss for a time. The rebel was being born!' These actions led to his hospitalisation, and because no illness could be found, he was written down as wrongly employed. Back at his Unit, he waited until his turn for leave arrived and he was sent home to England on his twenty-first birthday. Douglas then left the army with the idea of finding a new life in Australia. On the brink of departure, his father died, leaving Douglas grieving and with the task of settling his mother and sister in England.

Three major events then occurred: the Korean war was on the horizon, Douglas met and married his future wife and he was given his Commission back, but instead of being sent into defence he was posted to

West Africa. Health conditions were very bad there, and his young wife was unable to sustain the environment. Douglas endured his posting for eighteen months separated from her, exhausted and strained to his limit. The Africa experience was for him exactly like the India experience but at a greater level of intensity. 'I loved the army, but not the system by which it operated. My sympathy was with the African people and my inner tension grew as I literally conducted a private war against that system'. Douglas claims he would not have survived there at all had he not taken steps to tackle the issues that upset him. But in doing so he became ill, suffering a 'nervous break-down' which led to his return to England. Away from that tension, 'I recovered within days of this notable event, back at work in a tremendous job in a delightful country area.' This was the start of a phase of 'fabulous working years', promotion to the rank of Major and various postings leading to settlement in Australia.

Participation in the Vietnam war was upsetting, not the war in itself so much as the disappointing military standards and 'I concentrated on looking after my soldiers and at providing an attitude that would help them find laughter to ease their situation.' Once again, the inner struggle at this situation clearly caused an excess of tension, with accompanying anxiety being his personal expression of the frustration and anger he was feeling.

> I arrived home in Australia a very angry man, making myself unbearable to all and suffering recurring outbreaks of flu coupled with tremendous fatigue. I began to find it impossible to socialise and anticipatory anxiety at these events found its expression in hot spells and severe headaches.

Douglas finally left the army in 1976 after studying for an alternative career in Art and Building Construction. A fine artist, Douglas threw himself into painting and exhibiting his work and was very successful. But he began to suffer severe depression. 'Once again my feelings were at war.' The separation from his world of many years equated with 'loss of family and I struggled with civilian thinking and therefore, expectation'. Here again was a situation of powerful conflict, no doubt fuelling tension for him. 'On the one hand, though I detested many facets of it,

I was missing the Army a great deal, while on the other, I was now free to do as I liked yet somehow didn't know how to handle this.' He was referred to a psychiatrist who recommended medication. 'I knew this was not the answer. I started to drink alcohol, never heavily but daily, and the dependent habit developed.'

Seeking peace of mind and believing that to be the answer also to overcoming 'my lesser habits', Douglas attended intensive meditation in Melbourne with Dr Ainslie Meares. 'The result was absolutely beyond my greatest expectations. Something about Meares transported people beyond their pain. My return to good health and happiness was gradual, but decisive.' This lasted five years but began to fade when,

> . . . like so many other things in my daily routine I let my practice of meditation slip away and I just lost control of my life. I attended counselling for six years and tried hypnosis. I learned a lot about myself and how to handle situations, but I still worried. The effect of counselling was so temporary. Anxiety and depression plagued me and I lived with this, largely because of support from my understanding family.

Travel was also a source of relief and an opportunity to put his art to work. Douglas was unsettled, dividing his time between conducting a community workshop which he had initiated, his own artistic skills and his ongoing interest in aviation.

Four years ago, he experienced health problems involving his heart: fibrillation, spasms and a heartbeat of up to 130. This deterioration in health led to . . .

> my first serious panic attack. I felt disorientated and very frightened, especially at the experience of chest pain and visual disturbances. The diagnosis was asthma, arterial fibrillation and suspected blood clots. The treatment made me feel like an invalid — several different forms of medication, an asthma pump, routine hospital visits for extensive testing and various visits to specialists. I began to stay at home more and more — quite agoraphobic — and feeling extremely anxious and aimless. I was unable to clear my head of thoughts. I was greatly afraid of an asthma or heart attack or perhaps a stroke.

A retrospective of events reveals that the amount of stress Douglas experienced as a result of leaving the army was great indeed. 'I had no idea of just how different my life would be.' The earlier conflicting feelings he experienced within his profession and the persistent conflict between his desire to be free of the army and his difficulty in fitting into civilian life accelerated his fighting with tension and therefore an increase in anxiety. It is also apparent to him now that his life has been determined by movement and a belief that two or three years at most in any one posting is sufficient. Moving on, for Douglas, is energising. But on leaving the army, this movement had to cease and so for Douglas there was no escape, no prospect of re-energisation, possibly no prospect of hope — so a prevailing depression occurred.

At this point, Douglas approached me seeking 'peace of mind and with an aim to rejoin the human race'. He had known immense success from *stillness meditation* some years previously. Would it work for him again?

> This has been a sort of miracle really. I maintain daily meditation practice for up to an hour. After five months experiencing this form of meditation with you and practising at home, my heartbeat has returned to normal, that is, it now beats at 75 as opposed to 125. My doctor is amazed at my progress. I'm as healthy as any time, my mental approach is geared to my age and I am enjoying this 'rebirth'. And quality of life has returned to me. It seems incredible that to get to my first visit to you I had to battle with all the circumstances of driving that caused me nervousness. But now I drive around better than ever without a thought for worry. I'm at peace with the world and with things around me. That really sums it up. Even the things I don't like about my life. I'm at peace with them. My sense of humour has returned. I had lost a zest for life and all the things I couldn't do without extreme anxiety I'm doing now with delight. The stillness entices me to go the way I want — not the way of the world. I'm not religious but I am very, very spiritual. I know God sits on my shoulder, guides me at crossroads. Things always work out for the best.

By way of a message to others who are encumbered by tension, anxiety and depression, in summary Douglas says:

It is necessary to gain and retain complete control over your well-being, your mind and thoughts — and your physical health as well. And, be stubbornly truthful to yourself. It is not true to think you can't do certain things like drive the car freely, go to shopping malls, use public transport and attend social gatherings. The truth is, with adequate help and guidance, you can!

Jennifer

Jennifer's anxiety manifested in recurring panic attacks and she described symptoms which included claustrophobia, breathlessness, the fear of going crazy or dying in the midst of panic and a sense of being unable fully to trust herself. On a scale of 1–10, Jennifer estimated her anxiety level at 7 or 8. After two months' experience of *stillness*, this level dropped to 4 or 5.

> I have now been able to sense a life without panic attacks which is fantastic! I have a stronger sense of inner calm and feel more equipped to control anxiety. I am enjoying life more and gradually releasing my fear of panic attacks.

Two months later, we reviewed the situation again, finding her anxiety to be down to 3 or 4.

Jennifer is thirty-four, is married and a theatre performer. When we spoke at length, she readily admitted to having been brought up with an attitude of tension within the family.

> Alcohol was used as a way of coping for my parents, but in fact this dynamic only fed the existing tension and led to violent behaviour.
>
> At around the age of sixteen or seventeen, I became aware of what I perceived as a potential flaw in my nature. It was said within the family that I had my father's tempestuous nature. I saw this as a profound criticism of my personality and therefore I felt like I needed to hold myself back, as if holding in an angry monster. If I let myself be myself, this monster might run loose. From then on, I really felt quite on the back foot — unsure of myself and with my confidence rocked. I was so very afraid of myself, because I felt I could possibly hurt people. This was very shameful, so I began concealing that part of me from

the rest of the world. Being nice became very important to me.

As time went on, I discovered a very strong desire, like a force beyond myself really, to pursue theatre as a profession. The study of drama is so revealing — you really do face yourself and that began to stimulate my existing shame and fear. Perhaps my desire to make theatre my life was pushing me to seek and accept that other part of myself, because it was during this time that I became overwhelmed by panic. I was a student at drama school in Paris and although this was exciting, coping and studying in a foreign country presented many stressful issues to raise my tension level. Simultaneously, I gave up smoking marijuana. Giving up smoking meant giving up a way of managing my tensions. The change in physical environment and being cut off from people I knew helped trigger my crisis.

I was pretty desperate at that time really. Panic made me terribly afraid and I used to picture myself going out of control, being ugly, screaming, having a fit, frothing at the mouth and being seen to be a monster! It was very important that I keep that part of myself hidden. At that time, I began a personal journal and with support from a friend and a lot of reading, I spent a lot of time in self-analysis. This was very informative and I learned a great deal about myself, but the panic and the fear of panic remained constant.

Now I'm calmer. It's become easier and easier to become still and safe. Negative thoughts and anxieties have lost their grip on me. I have a general sense of being more centred. I feel something natural that's within me is gradually being uncovered. I haven't had a panic attack since commencing stillness meditation, whereas panic had been a regular part of my life. I especially notice how calm I am in various situations that I know once would have caused me anxiety. Also there are fewer swings in my tension level and those powerful images surrounding panic have passed.

I have also become more reflective, and I realise that reflectiveness is really very important. From this you can see a lot more about yourself and your life. I'm now finding that the things I need and want in life are coming to me, whereas before becoming experienced in stillness I was putting in a lot of effort to achieve. It all seems easier now. Even the tortures of life. My father has a serious illness and is slowly dying. In my grieving for him I had felt quite overwhelmed — as if I was somehow losing myself. Now somehow from the stillness I'm being helped to make some kind of sense of the journey of life and death.

I'm not so attached to things, not so caught up by the roller-coaster ride of latching on to issues and making them problems. Therefore I'm more able to observe these things and deal with them in a more positive way. And I have a little more courage to be myself. Because now I can see the link between my panic attacks and my fear of letting that shameful part of myself be seen. My fear really was that if I let that part of me out it would wreak havoc. Now I'm more accepting of that colour within my personality. I have also come to the major decision that I want to have a baby. I used to have a fear of getting lost again if I had a child. Now I feel stronger — more complete.

I'm realising that in stillness there is an opportunity to shift your belief systems and that the stillness gives you the calmness to do those things that we all think are so terrifying. The stillness takes great care of you and will not harm you. Out of this I can feel myself changing but on my own terms, my own sense of what is good or unhealthy for me. It is totally a worthwhile path to follow ... my life becomes better and better. I would not have been able to see, believe or trust such things six months ago.

Alley

At the onset of anxiety, Alley was nineteen and a second-year student at university. She had become overwhelmed by panic attacks resulting in agoraphobia, and 'felt very much alone with no idea of what was happening to me'. In recounting her typical symptoms, she reported 'feeling out of control with lots of irrational fears and stress waves'. Several significant events of a demanding nature had occurred in the preceding weeks and these had included the death of her grandfather.

I remember during the summer break, one very hot night I became dehydrated and experienced delirium. I felt absolutely awful —

scared! That seemed to be the crisis point and from then on, I was very unsure of myself — anxious all the time, afraid to be left alone, avoiding situations, terrified of driving my car and of leaving the familiarity of home. I was very dependent upon people close to me.

When we first met, Alley spoke of 'my mask of confidence but I'm frail inside. What people think of me is very important.' That was two years ago. Today, she says:

I've thought about my story in terms of the advice I'd give to others — let go of tension and change your mind! During my anxiety and agoraphobia I was lost. In a way I was partly lost before the anxiety. Now that I've come out of it I can look back over the experience and see my breakthroughs. I can also recognise that with a response of long-term tension it doesn't take much to push you to breaking point.

The first thing of importance I learned was patience. This was reinforced very strongly a couple of weeks after I began stillness meditation. I began that with the belief that my awful feelings would just go away and I would be back to 'normal', that is, back to where I was before the anxiety overwhelmed me. But soon I realised that the releasing effect of stillness was a gradual process. Then I learned the second important lesson: my anxiety wasn't coming from one single place or thing or even the way I was thinking about it, but it was a combination of matters tied together by my attempts to cover up a part of myself.

When we [she and I] started looking at my life I gained awareness that the anxious feelings were coming from notable moments from the past and that trying to overcome the anxiety as if it was just a current thing wasn't going to help much at all. What was going on currently were our clues to figure out the whole picture and those clues were somehow broken down as I released my tension level in the stillness of meditation.

The stillness was also like a place to work from and this was my third lesson: from the practice of stillness I could become free from anxiety and I could also change. I'm different now. There's more of me than there was before. Even before agoraphobia, I felt small, closed, withdrawn. My external appearance was normal, I'm sure. Others wouldn't have seen what was inside me. But my core, my kernel felt shrivelled, dark and closed. Now I feel bigger, as if my core is now touching my body. I feel closer to whole.

Alley's unacceptable part, the part of herself of which she was ashamed, was her childhood fear of staying away from home. Needless to say this fear had come from somewhere and she had invested great energy and, of course, tension, into concealing that part of herself. In early childhood she had experienced anxiety and tension at 'not being trusted'. By this she means that as a very little girl she felt excluded from knowledge or information with regard to a life-threatening illness suffered by her mother.

> I felt uncertain, bewildered, confused all the time. I wasn't a protected child but the not-being-told period of my life left me fearful and doubtful. So I wouldn't trust myself either. And this self-doubt led to my not being comfortable staying away from home. I saw this as very shameful and my sense of shame increased because, as time went on I realised that, while this behaviour could be acceptable from a little child, now I was an adult and still limited by my reservation. This was a huge inner pressure for me. I would become so tense about it that I would become physically sick. And I was tending towards losing control of my life because the issue kept coming up. Then, with all that tension, after several stressful incidents I was absolutely swamped by panic and then agoraphobia.

> It was really strange for me to become so reclusive because I had always been fairly outgoing and quite confident. I was a sensitive child, but confident, with a very strong, loving and supportive family. So I always had a good general self-esteem. In fact I believe it's when you have a good self-esteem that you want to hide what you haven't yet accepted about yourself. At that time the whole 'me' wasn't truly living. I was acting in a way — overcompensating for my limitation, and then feeling ashamed of the overcompensation as well!

> I had always pushed myself and this had worked for the most part. But of course I was pushing with tension which had only an exterior effect. It's not healthy to fight the immediate fear — you have to challenge the real thing. This fighting attitude didn't give me anything

of value — all it did was build my anxiety to the maximum. So I see now that it's pivotal to reduce the tension and to change what we believe about ourselves — that we don't have to fight and that limitations are an OK part of you too. Then you can change.

The first part of my change lay in learning to let go. This came through the meditative stillness. The next part of my change was to recognise where my shameful belief had come from and to accept that childhood fear as something I was now free to challenge in an adult manner. I continue to practise my stillness without fail each day, and over the past months as I relaxed mentally and learned to let go of tension more and more, the challenges I faced were much easier. I know now that letting go leads to wholeness in contrast to disintegration. When we're disintegrated we become smaller and smaller. But when we're more whole we can choose the bits we want in life and they become part of the expanding whole.

I've made great progress in the past two years. Being home alone is normal now, driving is easy and 'wild' social events, having fun, overnight stays, holidays with friends, uni camps and interstate flights have become part of a very full life.

As well as her personal achievements during this time, Alley's distinctions at university are evidence of a very capable young woman.

Also, I can now discern the things that hurt me or the things I don't want in life and make positive choices. Even death ... of those close to you which are so out of your control [Alley's life was touched substantially in this way during her recovery from agoraphobia.] ... you can choose how you deal with it, either with fear or with calm acceptance.

I've learned that having information is important to me. Even today if I sense people are keeping things from me it can be a sticking point. But today I don't succumb to this issue like I used to. I am free to act upon it. I now have the experience and the skills to, yes, be affected by life — but not break down, just bounce back. And I have a very strong sense of a future that holds a lot of positive living — **a great future!**

Theodore

I clearly remember when my first big panic attack occurred. It was 1998 and I was walking along a Melbourne street when I experienced a massive attack and collapsed.

An ambulance was called by a shopkeeper and when the paramedics arrived and examined me, they told me that I had 'only' suffered a panic attack. As they were leaving I clearly recall how frightened and vulnerable and helpless I felt. I also recall that when I asked "What should I do?" they suggested I book myself into a private hospital and in the meantime get myself onto some form of medication such as "Valium" to avoid a repeat of this incident.

After that day, my life became miserable, frustrating, very traumatic and extremely limited by agoraphobia. In fact my entire pre-occupation from 1998 until 2005 was to centre all my attention of every minute of every day in total avoidance of becoming stressed and/or suffering another panic attack — and without any hope of ever getting better and resuming the normal, happy and successful life I had previously known.

Then after an amazing and quite uncanny sequence of events, I literally stumbled across an old copy of *In Stillness Conquer Fear* and I found the courage to ring and to book myself an appointment with you. I have to say that making that appointment was not an easy task for me. In fact I didn't show up the first time because I became highly anxious on the way and turned the car around and went back home in fear and panic.

After getting over the embarrassment of that failed attempt I finally made it there. I can still clearly recall how uptight and frightened I was — literally shaking during that first consultation. Although I didn't get the full effect of the meditation on my first attempt that day I did however feel some calmness during the demonstration. Throughout the first weeks of my meditation course I was frightened and stressed at the beginning of most of those sessions, due mainly to my fear of being so far away from home. But gradually I found that I was able to let go and relax more and more, and I was becoming calmer and therefore slowly experiencing the full effect of this wonderful skill.

My first challenge took place some ten weeks down the track when I was called upon by friends to take them to the airport. Normally I would have instantly refused a request like this without even thinking twice about it. I had not been to Melbourne Airport for eight years and I don't need to tell you how concerned I was about the prospect of being stuck on a freeway without any escape routes – and a long way from home!

But I decided to meet the challenge and can clearly recall that the first five minutes on the freeway made me uneasy and quite scared. Strangely, though, I was not as frightened as I would have been before Stillness Meditation Therapy. Instead of panicking, I started to relax and in fact could quite clearly feel the effects of stillness actually "kick in", which gave me a comfortable drive that I actually enjoyed.

Aside from agoraphobia, I had also suffered from depression during those seven years, and as a result I had become a bit of a recluse during that time. Since that first journey away from my comfort zone, I have bought a 100 seat restaurant, and begun mixing with and being around people again on a daily basis. Even though the restaurant is very hard work, it has also been a major help in my recovery in that I have learnt to live and work quite freely at a high level of stress again. As a result both my body and my mind have adjusted to cope better with stress and anxiety.

At times, the journey of change was not always easy, but when one has enough desire to do something, it is amazing how you can find the strength and persistence to succeed – and therefore, to reclaim one's life! To gain, we need to persist and we need to let go of fear. Because the more we let it go, the more fear fades away as success grows from success.

Mardi

Since the age of seventeen Mardi had suffered depression, obsessional behaviour and agoraphobia. She had travelled the usual paths, seeking help.

Hers is a success story of great courage and an excellent example of the need for perseverance, especially in the practice of *stillness*, for at times she felt she was making no progress at all. When asked what was different about her life she laughed and replied enthusiastically,

> I've **got** a life — that's what's different! I remember the first time I came here. I was so anxious. I hadn't driven on a freeway for years and I thought I'd be an absolute mess during and after the session. But as soon as we talked together I knew this was the answer, this was what I had been searching for.
>
> There were times when things were really difficult — when I doubted *stillness meditation* and I was tempted to give up. But deep down I knew life had to be better. I just wanted to have some form of life, anything, to be able to live semi-normally. I used to be tense, anxious and withdrawn and very aggressive really. That's all in balance now. When I began to meditate regularly the aggression changed to determination.

Mardi's first big step to freedom came when she was able to drive to the beach.

> That occasion really stays in my mind. Going to the beach is some-thing you do as a kid ... when you haven't had that for a long time you want to get it back. So that trip was very important to me.
>
> I used to see agoraphobia and all those awful feelings as a kind of punishment. I know now that it wasn't something I did that caused me anxiety. I've learned to be more tolerant in life and I've learned that I am a good person after all. There have been dreadful dips along the way but I have always come out of them — as long as I maintain my stillness.

Mardi knew she had overcome agoraphobia when she was able to move out of the family home, buying her own together with her partner. Soon after, she made the commitment of buying a business, successfully estab-lishing herself in her own right in a field at which she excels.

> They were positive things to do, though 'scary' at the time. Making a big commitment is cause for anxiety for me, but I'm more able to deal with this aspect of myself. When I was anxious and agoraphobic I was child-like really. Now I feel strength, as if I'm an adult doing adult

things and being seen and treated by others as an adult. My partner is very supportive and is proud of my achievements. He has always encouraged me to move forward and not to give up.

I feel sorry for those people who do give up and succumb to anxiety as a part of their life. I can understand why they do — it seems easier. I can look back and recall a lot of panic and fear and pain and a lot of tears and confusion along the way. But because of that I've got my life back. I think now that the only thing to be afraid of out there is one's own vulnerability. I see myself today as a strong, calm, happy person — so different from the person you first met! And I'm not stopping here either. There's a lot more of life available and I'm going for that too.

John

John, a scientist, recorded his major symptoms at the time of his commencing *stillness meditation* as anxiety and compulsive thoughts. He rated his anxiety level at about 5 on a scale of 1 to 10; after seven weekly sessions this dropped to 2–3. He wrote the following:

> There is certainly more ease in my work and social life. I am more productive and more focused. Also, just recently, I have noticed a quite discernible change in the way other people relate to me. I find this amazing as I don't believe I have been behaving differently. Also the compulsive thoughts are greatly lessened and it seems that, slowly but surely, a more natural sense of security is coming to me.

Lorraine

A forty-two-year-old mother of two young children, Lorraine expressed symptoms of anxiety, stress, tension, panic attacks, agoraphobia and depression. These had been part of her life for the past nine years. She was taking regular medication and stated that one of her goals was to terminate this. Lorraine rated her anxiety level at more than 6; after eight weekly sessions she had successfully phased out the medication. She stated a greater sense of calm in the face of adversity together with greater clarity of mind: 'My unfounded fears are becoming less frequent and I am more relaxed generally.'

Lorraine also found herself communicating better with others and therefore making new friends. After sixteen weekly sessions, Lorraine estimated her anxiety level to have decreased to 2.

> After years of being unable to relax, I now truly can do so. I seem to know myself better as issues become clearer, and most importantly, I seem to be able now to harness the calmness at will.

When we last spoke together, Lorraine had commenced a course of study and was considering the possibility of part-time work.

Margaret

Margaret persisted with regular sessions in *stillness meditation* for well over two years, attending weekly, and for a generous length of time twice weekly. She had been suffering stress and anxiety for some time due to certain sadness in her life. She then developed quite severe depression, triggered by the loss of sight in one eye, the result of several operations and faulty surgery. Margaret's anxiety was accompanied by a 'constantly churning stomach'. She was taking several types of medication for her condition and was very keen to overcome her need for these. Even more significantly, Margaret's greatest wish was to regain her joy in living. She had tried another form of meditation and had not experienced any change to her well-being before taking the step towards stillness of mind.

When asked the question 'What meaning does the practice of stillness give to your life?', her answer related to her greatest wish:

> It's given my life new meaning. I enjoy each day again. I had lost interest in my garden and my home — and in doing anything much — and now I've regained all that. I love my garden and together with the time I put in to developing and maintaining that, I go each day to help at the library (a community organisation) helping people who are less fortunate than I am. The practice of stillness has just given me this desire that there's so much in life to do — and I didn't have that feeling before.

> The most important thing is that now I am calm when I go to bed. For a long time I couldn't sleep and was taking sleeping tablets, which

weren't helping me much at all. Now I don't take anything to sleep. I can just go to bed and I'm asleep in a few minutes and I sleep the whole night. It's all through *stillness meditation* that I'm able to live a normal life again.

Margaret no longer takes medication of any kind.

It took me all of two and a half years of regular sessions to get to this stage — until I just came to a point of tremendous change, when I really achieved what I believed would never occur. Now when I'm facing anxiety or in stressful situations I cope calmly. My problems and my life concerns are still there — but I approach them with serenity.

The remarkable point of this story is that Margaret is a beautiful and lively lady who has well exceeded her eightieth birthday. That years could not prevent her from faithfully persevering with so radical a form of therapy is commendable indeed. She above all must surely be deserving of the granting of her wishes!

Sharon

Agoraphobia had taken over Sharon's life at a time when her marriage was failing, reducing her to a state of disintegration and despair for at least seven years. A mother of (then) two teenage daughters, Sharon related this story of recovery.

I am a logical thinker, and I was trying to solve my problems in that manner. It was all very stressful and I fell apart. On bad days I could not leave the house at all. On good days I would manage to do things — always locally — with the help of Valium and with great difficulty. My reaction to agoraphobia followed the usual pattern: no spontaneity, no confidence, no pre-arrangement of events, no enjoyment and no independence. I couldn't participate properly in life with my family and, in short, I was a real pain.

I saw a psychiatrist for four years without any improvement to my condition. I went to a programme for agoraphobia sufferers, but it was totally drug-oriented and I didn't want that at all. A friend who was a psychologist helped in a supportive way, supplying me with literature and ideas, and from that assistance I decided to try a self-help group. Through that group I discovered behaviour therapy. That was very traumatic for me, but later it proved to have been useful. I was also introduced to the drug Xanax, but I was not interested in relying upon permanent medication. I settled for a mild tranquilliser that I could take, only when needed, as a crutch — something that would at least help me to do those things that were absolutely necessary, such as attending to the needs of my children.

My marriage had really ended by then, and my husband had left. So I had to look to the future of myself and my children and try to take some control of my life. At that time I realised that the behaviour therapy had helped, despite the trauma it caused, because at least it had familiarised me again with places I would never have gone to alone. That got me off the ground.

From reading your book, I discovered *stillness meditation*, and as you know, I began meditation sessions with you. Soon I terminated the behaviour therapy and gradually the tablets. I joined a women's study group which helped me understand a lot more about myself, and I was also attending your meditation sessions weekly and meditating regularly at home. It was becoming easier to leave the house alone.

After some months, I was able to make the decision to re-enrol at University to complete my Diploma of Education. The mere thought of a campus was quite overwhelming but, being a fiercely determined person, I told myself that I would try enrolment day and if I got through that, then maybe I could face the first lecture! Enrolment day brought a great deal of apprehension but nothing 'terrible' happened so I ventured further. Success built on success. I got to the lectures and achieved excellent results. During that time I was offered a part-time teaching job, and accepted it. With my duties as mother and housekeeper, plus studying and the part-time work, I often felt great exhaustion. So I took pains to compensate for the fatigue with lots of rest and lots of meditation in between. My confidence gradually built more and more.

I feel now I am a person who has regained a lost part of myself. I am now more like the person I was fifteen years ago and am unrecognisable as the agoraphobic I was for seven years. I have boundless energy and enjoy everything I do — sometimes I experience a sense of wonderment at it all.

The Chinese characters for 'crisis' can be interpreted as change and opportunity. That really impresses me. When crises occur they are usually associated with illness, depression, anxiety or marital problems. To experience agoraphobia means you have been given an opportunity to learn and to change. And it's absolutely true that there is no gain in life without pain. I believe overcoming fear is a combined process of reducing the tension and anxiety and getting to know yourself. The rest falls into place. Now I understand my strengths as well as my weaknesses. And I have also come to see and accept those parts of me that I don't like. The total experience has also given me more of an insight into others too, and into my expectations of others. I've come to realise that together with the parts I do like in myself and others, what I don't like adds to the richness of the whole.

It's OK now if I don't live up to old expectations. No-one has to be perfect. In the course of recovery, I happened to meet a young woman who had lost the use of her legs and was confined to a wheelchair. She amazed me by sharing the thought that if her greatest wish could be granted and somehow she could have her legs back, she would refuse. She was adamant that in losing her legs she had gained a hundredfold in strength, tolerance and self-knowledge. And that's how I feel about my experience of agoraphobia. During my years of fear, I used to have frustrating dreams that I was in the city, or driving here or there and I'd wake up thinking, 'Hey, I shouldn't be in those places.' Now it's as if my dreams have become the reality and what my actual dreams contain is just peace and togetherness.

Sharon successfully completed that part of her study and the last time we met she was working three days a week as an administrator in a support organisation. In her work she was recruiting and training staff members, and driving anywhere and everywhere to interviews. She was also teaching two days a week at a tertiary level and furthering her own qualifications in relevant fields. With agoraphobia long forgotten and having spent a month in Europe on a holiday, Sharon now felt free to travel wherever her dreams might take her.

Susie

Susie was stricken with panic when she was seventeen and was severely inhibited by agoraphobia for over seven years. She was unable to leave the house unaccompanied, or to remain at home alone. To her extreme credit, she had never swallowed a tablet in her search for freedom. Her persistence and her determination to succeed in the face of what some would regard as insurmountable obstacles along the way was quite remarkable.

> I think the most important step you take towards getting better is when you realise that the only person who can really help you is you; and that you've really got to learn to trust yourself, rely on yourself and not fear yourself. I suppose once you've learned those things then you have to believe them, and that's the hard part — the part I haven't quite mastered yet.
>
> I used to believe that the anxiety I felt was mostly involuntary, but I realise now that my frame of mind, my attitude to life and the thoughts I make happen are the things that trigger or cancel out the anxiety. I guess in a way that's how the meditation works. It helps your mind become calm and enables you to make the choice — to stay calm, as you do in stillness, or give in to your old patterns and gather up all the ingredients to pave the way for a good old panic session.
>
> It [stillness] is also important because it's yours. You own it and control whether you do it or not. It's a kind of gift you give yourself, even though at times the prospect of doing it can feel like a chore. But it's the times when it doesn't feel like a chore or a duty that are good. It's a back-up, a support too. If I don't do it I feel more vulnerable. When I've done it, I'm calmer and I feel as though I have the edge over things.
>
> All these strange sensations really do inhabit everyone's lives at some stage (to a lesser extent perhaps), but they are all normal ways of expressing, feeling or dealing with anxiety. People really are very complex and, also, very ignorant of the way they function or malfunction.

Because those feelings seem to occur in your head (or your heart) you can believe you can't escape from them. Often I wished I could take a holiday from myself, hang my head up in the wardrobe and take off without it. The people who mean most to me rate very highly in my heart and I react quite easily to the ups and downs they trigger. But that's me and I'll always care too much, worry too much — but I think that's OK, as long as I can accept it and carry on regardless.

There are too many books around that tell you how to become more loving, forgiving, happier, wealthier, successful, and so on. These books give people in crisis false expectations of themselves and the future. Dr Meares, however, was different. I get a lot out of his writing because he points people towards themselves; no ideals, just the desire to be at ease with yourself, and that's the most important thing people must learn. It's OK not to be perfect, but it's not OK to always feel ill at ease with yourself. That's what Dr Meares was meaning.

It's good to draw on experiences you've had in your own life for comfort. When I'm not really feeling like approaching a challenge but nevertheless know I have to take the plunge, I remember back to when I was little. I was a very late swimmer and didn't learn until I was twelve or thirteen years old. When I finally got up enough courage to bob under the water and then let go of the edge, I realised there was nothing to it, and the biggest problem was the fear I had of actually letting go of the edge. Once I did that, there was nothing to worry about at all!

How simple to let go — when we know how! It took two and a half years of regular attendance at meditation sessions and a great deal of encouragement and support along the way for that young butterfly to emerge from her chrysalis. From her first faltering steps to the corner shop, she blossomed to enjoy full-time employment in a field suitable to her creative talent. Later she completed her degree, qualifying as a teacher before marrying and moving interstate.

Elisabeth

The progress made by this woman, a primary teacher, in a relatively short period of time was quite remarkable. Elisabeth had been agoraphobic for over twenty years and was completely housebound when her husband first accompanied her to consult me. She commenced regular attendance at meditation sessions and persevered well with her regular practice at home.

> Not only had I endured the effects of agoraphobia for all those years but I eventually developed a fear of being anywhere alone, even in my own home. My mind was forever in a state of panic, and this made life extremely difficult.
>
> I tried various treatments including eight weeks in hospital, private psychologists and an organised programme for anxious people. Each of those forms of treatment contributed something in helping me understand my difficulty. Despite each, I remained in a stable, but fearful, state. I began to realise that the problem was within myself. I was the only one who could help me! At about that time I read your book and after eighteen months of meditation I am now able to stay at home alone and enjoy the peace and quiet that solitude offers. I feel quite comfortable in crowded places and shopping centres again. My greatest triumph is my return to part-time work in my former profession and I find the practice of stillness helps me greatly in this.
>
> I still have some hurdles to overcome. My next goal is to learn to drive again so that I can work on venturing further while unaccompanied. This is not easy to pursue at present, since there is no public transport in our area.
>
> I now have every confidence that with patience and determination — and regular practice of stillness — I will succeed in fully overcoming fear and find freedom, serenity and independence.

The last time I saw Elisabeth I was struck by her ease and the composure glowing in her face, as opposed to the haunting, straining tension and anxiety that had been so apparent on our first meeting.

Kris

This young woman developed agoraphobia following attacks of giddiness and blurred vision each morning, noticing these symptoms first while driving to work. Thinking her eyes were at fault, she consulted an optometrist.

My sight was said to be perfect, but the problems remained. I visited my general practitioner and was prescribed medication for a sinus condition. This treatment made no difference. The giddy feelings and visual disturbances increased. I began to avoid leaving the house and didn't want to drive the car, because these activities seemed related to the unpleasant way I was feeling. I became very depressed ... weepy all the time. I believe the depression was a result of being at home so much and not knowing or understanding what was causing it all.

My general practitioner was lovely. I can't speak highly enough of him. He was helpful, tolerant and sympathetic. He was a kindly, elderly gentleman who went out of his way to assist me while trying to solve the problem. He often made home visits because I was unable to go to him. And later, when I had progressed a little, he would let me know exactly when to be at his surgery to spare me the dreaded waiting that phobic people find so difficult. At this time this doctor prescribed anti-depressants and minor tranquillisers — and I really needed them. There is a place for this kind of medication, at least for that time when it's virtually impossible to cope without it.

The medication enabled me to achieve such trivial things as going outside to my letter box. I was determined to win this battle, and in time I could walk to the corner, a few houses away. I tried driving and could only manage a trip around the block (certainly no traffic lights!). But I continued to persevere anyway. My sister was marvellous. She has experienced similar symptoms throughout her life — though not agoraphobia — and she would accompany me in my experimental outings. Often I came out of a shopping centre in tears.

A lot of time passed and I was really not progressing. So (against my doctor's advice) I decided to consult a psychiatrist. This man seemed very highly regarded and I felt confident that I was doing the best thing. It surprised me though, that his rooms were on the top floor of a tall building! Only my sense of humour got me through those visits. My sister was with me. She dislikes enclosed places, so by the time we had left the elevator we were both crying and sweating and shaking. Then we would observe other patients arriving in a similar state!

The psychiatrist prescribed drugs to reduce my anxiety and at the same time took me off all other medication. I had suffered from high blood pressure long before any of these anxiety problems emerged, and for years I had taken tablets to control that. Now I was to take nothing but the tablets prescribed by the psychiatrist. I persevered with them and I really believed that one day I would wake up calm and peaceful and completely free of anxiety and all the awful symptoms that had become part of my life. Unfortunately, the opposite occurred. Without the necessary medication, unknown to me my blood pressure soared. And my anxiety, rather than disappearing, was increasing rapidly until depression returned once more. I was visiting the psychiatrist weekly. He kept telling me that it would take time to improve ... while increasing the dosage. But my anxiety was becoming worse. I was sleepless, my heart was thumping dreadfully all the time and I became worried that there was something seriously wrong with me.

The crunch came one day when I began having blackouts, so I decided to go to a hospital, and by the time I arrived I was unable to walk properly. In the casualty section that day, my blood pressure was 240/140 and the staff on duty could hardly believe I was still alive! When I showed them the medication I was on, and they later had it analysed, it turned out that all those tablets I had taken in good faith were only placebos. I was terribly ill — and I have never forgiven the psychiatrist his treatment. In all, I had lost twelve months of potential progress and I was now back to square one: blood pressure tablets, anti-depressants, Valium. After my blood pressure stabilised, I sought avenues for counselling and therapy. Unfortunately these made no difference to my symptoms. However, through one psychologist I came to realise that if I wanted to get out of this mess, it was up to me to make it happen.

Then I read your book and wrote to you for information about learning meditation. I had previously thought that such 'pastimes' were ridiculous, but I was prepared now to try anything. It took months of sessions before I even 'got the hang' of what was meant by stillness. I feel sure that for this reason many people give meditation away before they achieve anything. But I persevered, with a positive desire to recover from the situation I was locked into.

My husband, and later my sister, used to drive me to the sessions. Little by little, things began to improve. I was able to cut down the medication and my GP was very pleased to see the change in my progress. I was too fearful to drive, but started to ride a bike and found this a very useful way of getting out a little. After a time I took on a small job, door-to-door selling, not for the income but to make progress and gain confidence. I joined the local gym and would run down for a quick aerobic class and then run home again, about three times a week. Soon I began to enjoy these times. One day, surprisingly, I was offered a part-time job there, teaching aerobics. I took the job, and although at times this commitment wasn't easy for me, the rewards were great. So after some months of work I decided to enrol for a two-year teacher training course in the fitness industry. When filling out the enrolment form I had no idea how I could travel that distance to the college on a regular basis to complete the course — but I wanted to do it, and I did.

My life was becoming busier. Now I was running classes, studying, finding freedom in general life, and meditating. I passed my first year and things were definitely looking better. I went on to second year, completed my first aid course and decided to buy my own car. At the end of that year I qualified as an aerobics and gym instructor, so I applied for a position in a large fitness organisation. After six months there, I was so confident that I was promoted to gym manager! I have now been working in that role for two years. I take no medication, not even for blood pressure — there is no need to.

My greatest interest now is running, and my greatest achievements have been in running marathons. I have raced among 40,000 people and finished in the top third. Physical activity is what I most enjoy.

I have no regrets about having experienced agoraphobia. It has given me a greater tolerance and sensitivity to the needs of others. I have learned that each of us is on our own and life is what you make it. There were probably things in my childhood that contributed to my phobia, but I don't think that is the important issue. The best people to help sufferers of anxiety are those who have experienced something of the kind themselves. It's almost impossible to understand the feelings and symptoms if you've not known them yourself. And I have always told others about my former problem. I have never been ashamed of it in itself and I think this attitude helps in overcoming it.

Sometimes I feel anxious — I'm sure everyone does at times — but this anxiety is nothing at all compared with those phobic years. I'm really interested in this problem and some day I would like to help other sufferers.

My mind had never been quiet for a moment until I learned to meditate. I would like to see stillness taught in schools. It's very difficult to break all those bad habits of tension when you've been repeating them for years. Life would be far simpler if people were introduced to meditation in childhood as part of the day's routine. The experience of stillness opened the door for me and now I have completely changed my direction. I love my career and I am very happy.

The last time I saw Kris she had three ambitions: to start her own business in the fitness industry, to continue with further study and to win a veteran marathon — after her fortieth birthday!

George

An architect in private practice, George made the following comments after attending several sessions in *stillness meditation*.

I haven't felt panicky since I started here four weeks ago. I'm practising every day at home and this change in my life is fantastic! I just 'shut myself down' and all's well. I haven't enjoyed life so much for years.

Gloria

A client of many years who still calls in for an occasional time of stillness,

Gloria defined her changes in the following narrative. When we first met, anxiety and severe depression were paralysing her life.

My life has been lived in two distinct phases — thirty-five years before *stillness meditation* and fifteen years after. The effect of daily stillness in my life has been profound. Not in an earth-moving, bell-ringing sort of way, but in an inner strength sort of way. From my early childhood, through my school years into adulthood, marriage and the birth of my children, I lived with a very high level of anxiety. There were many life experiences along the way to contribute to that but this is only known to me in hindsight and the wisdom of my 'new' life.

This new life too, has thrown many, many challenges my way. Serious health problems for myself and my husband, the demands of teen-age children and a myriad of problems too numerous to mention. But my new life gives me a new thread which runs through me at all levels — spiritual, emotional, intellectual and physical. Now I am strong. I know myself and I am in touch with my inner voice. There is a peaceful equanimity in my life and fear has taken a back seat. I have a happy and rewarding family and fulfilling employment at a breast cancer clinic.

I have discovered a small talent for writing poetry which joyfully expresses my view of the world — a contrast indeed to years in my 'old' life where I never truly saw the world around me. And I play golf at weekends along with other hobbies. My 'new' life is full to the brim, almost overflowing with an ease I had not known before. There is joy and laughter, sadness and tears in this life ... but it is my life, my season in the sun.

Isabelle

Isabelle, a senior teacher and faculty head, was on sick leave when we first met. Three months later she wrote this to me:

I realise that I have lived in a nervous, anxious state for most of my life, always having quite unrealistic expectations of myself. I have managed my life by working harder and harder, keeping my mind and body always tense and busy. Although the years have provided many moments of happiness, I can certainly see now that I have made life very hard for myself.

After the death of both of my parents and a close friend, my nervous tension and general anxiety increased greatly and resulted in some dreadful feelings. I began to experience panic attacks. I felt agitated for much of the time, constantly tired and unable to eat or sleep properly. I experienced periods of rapid heart rate and overwhelming fear. I was terrified and could not understand what was happening to me. My doctor was very sympathetic, encouraging the use of tranquillisers. He offered no alternatives and said if I did not take medication to reduce the symptoms, I would need to be hospitalised. I believed that there had to be another solution. Somehow I knew that I was responsible for my condition and therefore I had to be responsible for helping myself.

Then I remembered that my brother had found relief from his anxiety in *stillness meditation*. After committing myself to classes and home practice I could barely believe how quickly I began to improve. All those symptoms started to disappear. My doctor could not believe how quickly and how much my health improved.

After three months I have learned and experienced so much. I can relax, I can enjoy moments of stillness. I live my life more calmly. I approach problems more objectively. I appreciate everything in my world in a different way. I know that regular practice of stillness will be part of every day to come and I look forward to continuing along the positive and peaceful road I have found. I certainly have not stopped there — but I know that this skill has changed my life and given me confidence to free myself from the past and move to the future, living my life more fully and experiencing ongoing tranquillity. That my tension and anxiety were lowered so quickly and easily is still puzzling at times — so simple, yet so effective.

In closing this chapter, Sandra chose to express the changes brought by *stillness meditation* in her special artistic way:

Sandra

Meditation distils the murky waters of my emotion, thoughts and
anxiety.
By just sitting in the stillness . . . clarity comes
and its presence is felt on all levels and beyond time.
The stillness, the calm, the silence
naturally bring peace
like a fresh breeze soothing and awakening my soul.
I feel connected to myself,
not fragmented, but whole.
I can feel and be, just naturally
without rational analysis or judgment
and this is so liberating . . . I feel much healing in this 'just being'
without the 'thinking' our culture is so obsessed with.
It's an art, a way of knowing and being
far deeper than words or thoughts could ever take me.
It really is a matter of just sitting down and slipping into my inner
world
. . . ceasing the doing
. . . letting go of the thinking
. . . going beyond my familiar zone
. . . and into my Being
and then the magic begins . . .

What happens while I'm there I can't say
because it is silent there
and Sacred too.
Enough to say it feels like the very core of life
the very place of Being
where healing happens
where life is built
where paths are corrected and set straight.

It is a Sacred space.
Not one I necessarily 'go' to,
but one which is already there
A calm within my centre.
I just 'be' in the stillness and allow

the outer layers of thought, action, worry and tension to peel away
little by little, layer by layer.
Until . . . I am with myself
unguarded, uncluttered, unencumbered
Simply Me.
It feels comfortable, easy,
the essence of wellness, inner peace, harmony.

And yet, it reaches far deeper and way beyond just Me.
It feels mysteriously connected to all of Life,
A oneness shared by all.
I am Home.
I will reach my fullness.

PART FOUR

Reflections, Observations and Growth

Chapter 16

A PERSONAL REFLECTION

❧

This Quiet, all it hath a mind to do, doth.

Robert Browning

The click-click of my heels on the tiled floor was the only sound that echoed throughout the massive structure of grey stone. I had been walking to my car from a meditation session at Dr Meares' rooms and, moved by my having gained the wonder of tranquillity in an otherwise noisy and congested city, I impulsively detoured from the sunshine outside into the chill quiet of the cathedral. And here, in another setting of peace, I stopped to contemplate the disappearance of my past companion, fear, and to give thanks for the *ease of being* that had emerged from stillness, improving the quality of my life in a myriad of ways.

In musing over those earlier years, my thoughts drifted back to the first time I experienced panic and to all that had occurred in the months preceding it. A great deal of stress had come my way and I did cope with it, but I coped with it in a state of tension and therefore I did not cope well. It was little wonder, then, that my anxiety soared and that I experienced a memorable attack of panic — which scared the 'living daylights' out of me and led to agoraphobia.

The belief that we must fight stress is a common one. Obviously I had picked up this belief and at the onset of stress I certainly fought with all my might. New responsibilities, worries and concerns had entered my world, and one way or another had caused me restlessness and a sense of pressure. Rather than *listening* to those responses, I braced myself against them. I was very good at bracing myself. I had practised the response of bracing myself, steeling myself and fighting discomfort to the point that I had become a virtual master at it. I knew how to pretend to the world that all was well when in fact my inner self was hurting. How had this come about? Sitting that day in the stillness of the cathedral led me to wonder about my life's journey thus far. And so, with the practice of stillness ever supporting me — in fact, *guiding* me — I began a reflective search over my former years, exploring and defining those aspects of my life which had been obstacles in my path and may have contributed to my experience of agoraphobia. In this search I discovered the jewels of stillness, diamonds rough and smooth: the pain and the joy of getting to truly know myself.

My starting point lay within the element of tension itself. Former treatment offered for my phobia had been centred upon anxiety, taking the line of approach that my fear of leaving home was caused by significant issues from my early childhood — either a severe fright or an unresolved conflict. In reviewing this approach, none of these recollections means to imply criticism of the medical treatment I received at the onset of my phobia. For it is true that from alarming events and difficult conflicts much anxiety can be born. And, as I now began to see, like many others I was indeed carrying unresolved conflicts. And yes, the psychoanalytic form of treatment for anxiety can bring relevant past issues to consciousness where they can be understood and dealt with and this may assist in alleviating emotional pain.

But at the time I was seeing the psychiatrist, my tension level was so high and my mask to the world (himself included) was so securely in place that it was impossible for deeper insight to open to me. Even *had* I gained that knowledge then, it would not have been the magical wand I needed to dispense with my phobia — of that I am certain. For these issues in themselves were not so severe; it was my personal way of coping, my fighting, that was keeping symptoms active and me ensnared. Any former treatment I received had apparently not considered the governing influence of tension, the counterpart to anxiety.

Now, through stillness, I was able to see that agoraphobia was the way I had adopted to defend myself against something I feared. Stress had increased my anxiety (a response to a fear within myself, though as yet unidentified), producing the symptoms of which I was afraid, so to avoid these symptoms, and any danger those symptoms might bring, I fought with tension. I did not recognise that element of expression —

for expression it is, since tension speaks its own language — until Ainslie Meares spoke those words to me at my initial consultation with him: 'You are rather tense . . .'

I remember the instant he made that statement. Subdued by fear for the previous eight years, I had felt myself to be a lesser person, a weak person and a kind of failure in life. At Dr Meares' words, one part of me felt greatly relieved; for an excess of tension seemed much more acceptable than personal weakness as a reason for my phobia. But there was a flicker of doubt within the other part of me. It all seemed too simple. And yet, of course he was right. Through my newfound vision, it was obvious to me that my old automatic response to life — and thus agoraphobia — had come about in that way, tension in my body, but more importantly, tension within my mind. With agoraphobia now behind me, I began to explore my beginnings.

That little girl who had wandered joyfully in her next-door neighbour's garden was, I am certain, relatively tension free — and quite confident. There were protective rules and restraints upon my life, of course. But generally speaking, I was then a blithe spirit. Being the elder of two girls by almost four years, I had also the knowledge of a certain kind of freedom. No doubt the arrival of my sister interrupted this flow, but I have no memory of any animosity towards her. On the contrary, she was someone to share my life with. In those early years, we had no immediate cousins or young friends and neighbours, so we relied greatly upon each other for company and for intimate childish play. They were happy years. And yet at times life was unpredictable. For my mother was not a relaxed person.

As a child, I was sometimes troubled when my mother appeared to be 'harassed' (her word) — but I didn't realise then that she was *tense*. She was quite flamboyant and could be dramatic, speaking her worries aloud, usually about the fact that her blood pressure was too high. This concerned me and I somehow felt responsible for her well-being. But among her many gifts, my mother was fairly optimistic and had at her fingertips the ability to enjoy a sense of humour, fun and nonsense, accompanied by ready peals of laughter. So while on the one hand she demonstrated worry, on the other she brushed her worry aside and busied herself as usual. Never would the world at large have guessed her uneasy feelings. Now, in hindsight, I could see that she was quite tense, but concealed this under that mantle of busyness and good humour; only we at home sensed her intermittent discomfort. In her capacity to cover her tracks, she taught me to do the same while raising certain queries in my child's mind. She also ignited that sense of doubt within my soul: was she really likely to become seriously ill? Was illness something that didn't occur so long as you laughed? How do you judge whether illness is serious or not … *how do you really know what's going on … ?*

The emotional lessons I learned from my father were of another stalwart kind. By nature he was more reserved than my mother, a very strong though sensitive and gentle man who pondered philosophical theories and read literature; a man who was internally frustrated by not having realised his vocational potential. His affliction of deafness, the onset of which occured in his twenties, I later recognised as immensely distressing and a powerful source of tension for him. Generally speaking, I think the suffering and the isolation of the deaf is not always comprehended by others as the onerous problem that it is. In particular — and this must have caused him great pain — spontaneous communication with his two little girls was practically impossible. The shared moment, the whispered word, the intimacy of family togetherness were largely lost between our father and us children. He withstood his loss in silence, bracing himself against the hurts in his world, and covertly teaching me to do the same. If some of my mother's characteristics contributed to a little insecurity within me, my father's presence compensated for that, and he betrayed no hint of his distress. But his tension was evidenced by the strain mirrored in his eyes.

Our maternal grandmother lived with us in my early years, an indomitable character who largely 'ruled the roost'. I don't believe she created problems for us children, but I do think her company contributed to tension between my parents and the wholeness of their relationship. Such issues were never openly discussed. Intuitively, though, I sensed their existence and knew that, at times, one had to tread carefully. These three figures were of course, the major influences in my early years. And then there was Nessa, whom I have earlier described. If I enjoyed many hours enchanted under the spell of her garden, she also enjoyed many hours enjoying the warm hospitality of our kitchen table. Together with my aunt who visited regularly, Nessa and other women friends of my mother's provided dominant adult company, a very secure daily life and an extended family experience which is not so commonly found today. Within this tender and pleasant environment, as recalled earlier in this book, fear could be easily forgotten. It was a deeply loving home, but with the truth of hindsight, the use of tension around me was, in subtle ways, established as a reality.

The practice of stillness, seedlike, produced memories of my starting school that were not so pleasant. Having had no experience in interacting with other children or the rough and tumble of the playground, Preparatory class and Grade 1 were something of a nightmare. I felt very lonely, different from the rest and quite shy. This was unusual for me, because at home I had the reputation of enjoying an audience as I 'held the floor' — singing songs and reciting nursery rhymes by heart from a very early age and receiving much attention for my efforts. Now, suddenly, at school such posturing was not permissible — nor, under the circumstances did I feel any inclination to perform in that way. My first lesson at school was an introduction to inhibition!

Here I believe, was where my own tension began to arise. As my parents did each in their way, I too began to pretend. It seemed important to *appear* to be learning easily, enjoying myself, making friends, demonstrating ease and comfort; but I was definitely struggling and alerting my tension more and more to assist me in that struggle. My mother was generous in her attentiveness to this insecurity, but her presence, though comforting, also caused me great discomfort and metaphorically pulled me in two directions. This created another kind of tension — a conflict of interests: my need for security and my embarrassment at having that need satisfied. *The result of this was an intricate mix of confusion, embarrassment and shame very similar to the feelings that accompany and maintain the agoraphobic response.*

Unfortunately, teachers in those times were often intolerant of the whims of young children. I remembered only impatience or indifference from my teachers, never compassion. It seemed too that I could never please those teachers. In being 'good', I was often humiliated in the classroom by adults who ought to have known better. And then, if occasionally I ventured into the realm of naughtiness, I would be strongly reprimanded, punished and told that such behaviour was not like me at all. Confusion! I was a well-behaved child, but I wasn't a 'wimp' — and I wasn't stupid either. Although sensitive and often hurt by these adults, I could see right through them and their ways. But the young child cannot match the power of the adult; nor does the child have words to communicate such observations, and so in this it seemed I had to fight a lone and silent battle.

An inherent strength or stubbornness pushed me to prove myself beyond these no-win situations, tilting my tension level up a little more to do so. I pressed on with my school work and was successful. In the course of this success, I also cemented wonderful friendships with my peers and forgot the insecurity of my early days. But I know now that elevated tension was by then becoming a way of living for me and I had also learned some more negative beliefs: it was shameful to have personal needs; I must remain on guard; I was the sole defender of myself; and there were many people I could not trust — most obviously, those powerful adults outside the home.

Generally happy, but carrying these beliefs, I continued at school to the time for secondary education. This evolution coincided with a financial crisis for my father and to my dismay, my parents' concern for the future prevented me from making the transition to senior school with my peers. Concurrent with this, a particularly influential teacher had used her power to exclude me from sitting a scholarship examination which may well have changed the situation (and the course of my life).

Today, that turning point might categorise me as a victim of discrimination, but I lay no blame. People do the best they can with the abilities they have at the time. As it has all turned out, my life is better for having learned all this which only proves to me that we all have a destiny to follow and that whatever occurs during one's life, occurs for good reason. As it happened, my story led me with only one companion from primary school to enrolment elsewhere. Again, bravado rescued me — for I felt largely on my own again — but this time I was armed with new beliefs and of course, my established weapon of tension to deflect a smouldering anger at the injustice of this turn of events.

In spite of my initial disappointment, the schooldays that followed were very happy, productive and anxiety-free. But now, after the introduction of stillness into my life, a greater understanding of the pain surrounding that experience was revealed to me. I was able to see that this untimely separation — in my most formative years — from the achievements I had made at school and the strong relationships I had built there, hurt me intensely. Buried within the deepest part of myself, my psyche or soul, the idea grew that I was less worthy and less competent than the rest of my friends, to some extent a kind of failure. This idea fuelled the subtle shame I had already learned, and at that time I felt publicly humiliated and similarly judged by others.

Here was a critically negative experience to fight against, needing much more tension to drive me; I feel this was the point when I completely assimilated tension into my life, believing it to be normal and a useful way to live. Clearly, from early childhood through adolescence and beyond, stoic fighting from within was the attitude I had adopted to help me in my lone and silent journey through conflicts, questions, insecurities, doubts, injustices, losses, hurts and misgivings. And so I employed that same inclination to fight in an effort to preserve *the integrity of my own identity.* I was driven to prove myself a worthy person by concealing what I believed was shameful about me.

It is noteworthy that none of these difficulties in my life was unique to myself. The tapestry of most people's lives is woven from such matters, or worse. Certainly I was fortunate in that I had experienced no cruel assault or abuse from which to become anxious. However, the difficulties that I could not identify were influences in my young life to which I responded with aversion. And I had learned (as do many other people), to deal with difficulties in a way that was unhelpful and in a way that set me up for a later crisis. Also, I had accumulated more negative beliefs: that deep personal feelings were of no consequence, and that it was best to disregard my own needs and give attention to pleasing others.

As we live each day, our brain is constantly receiving information and responding accordingly at both a conscious and unconscious level. If our general level of tension has increased too much, the mind becomes over-stimulated, too alert. Then our anxiety also increases, bringing with it feelings of agitation, restlessness and an attitude of being keyed up, unable to relax.

This was certainly my developing reaction in the years that followed. With education completed (tertiary at that time was not an option for me), my working life was happy, my family life was secure, I enjoyed great, fun-filled friendships and a splendid social life, I was bright and cheerful and my creative interests were richly fulfilled. But inwardly, subtle anger in the form of negativity simmered, and tension kept me on guard. Determined to prove my worth and ready to defend myself against my perceived threat of potential humiliation, so significant was my 'face to the world' that I held my feelings within and refrained from seeking direction from parents or mentors. This reaction resulted in a number of life choices and decisions that were not truly my own and which, in retrospect, eventuated in a kind of vicarious living where in time my husband's presence in my life began to compensate for what I believed I lacked in myself.

And then the happiness of early married life was interrupted by the advent of my father's sudden death and a chain of further sad happenings. Under stress, physically and emotionally exhausted, and carrying many responsibilities at that time, my anxiety increased, sending me messages — or symptoms — of a need to care for myself. When I missed these messages or refused to listen, the symptoms culminated in panic — *an out of control experience*.

To maintain a sense of security, all people have the need to feel that their life is in control. Within my reflections I came to see that my use of tension over many years was an unconscious and misguided striving for control and a way of dealing with the positive and negative beliefs I held within my heart, psyche or soul.

In that appraisal of myself I had, in a way, split myself into two parts. One part I could positively appreciate and value. The other, the part I was ashamed of, was largely fashioned from my own imaginings. I had viewed normal human vulnerability as unworthiness or personal weakness, representing failure which panic would fully expose. My negative beliefs told me that if this failure was exposed, I would be open to unfavourable judgment (and probably rejection) from other people. I *must* defend myself. And this meant *myself* in total. I must fight to preserve the part of me that I appreciated and wanted others to know — and I must also fight to prevent the other part from public exposure. The shame of some final reckoning and total humiliation, should that 'failed' part of me be fully let loose as the end result of a panic attack, loomed largely. But the more I fought, the more panic assailed me — and the more I needed a safe haven … my husband's presence, my home, my car … each safe place being affirmation of me as an acceptable human being. Here then was my conflict, the battle *within* myself that I had sought in vain outside myself to understand.

In my defensive fighting, I had lost control of my life to the limiting life of fear. The true control of one's life does not happen this way. As I became more tranquil and my mind became clearer, I was able to see that there was no need to go to such lengths in self-preservation. In fact, I had been my own worst enemy. Now I was able to look back and know that I was probably not significantly judged by others. I expect I was quite well accepted and appreciated as a person, as much as any other. But carrying the belief that part of me was unworthy and trying desperately to prove this otherwise, I had developed a life attitude of inner defensiveness. And so I had lost true control until, from within stillness and learning to 'let go', clarity like a golden sword pierced the mist surrounding me. As I became at ease *within* myself, I became at ease *with* myself.

With a calmer mind, I began to identify fear as poison to the soul. In fear I had disowned a part of my whole being and in so doing, I had judged myself very harshly. With this attitude and its accompanying tension, any of my personal limitations became, for me, unacceptable. I was unconsciously striving for perfection. But perfection is a pipedream; it does not belong to the reality in which we live. All human beings have their frailties, weaknesses, brokenness. These are part of our story and they represent our truth. It is only in acknowledging our limitations that we can fully accept ourselves as we are, and then set about the enduring task of changing and growing. I had to learn this.

For I had only been prepared to accept one part of myself, the part that (in my view) would show up all right under public scrutiny. By trying to keep control over hiding the rest of me, I was denying the truth of myself and therefore I was only half alive! Because, whenever the other unacceptable part looked like making an appearance, my anxiety would soar and I would run for cover. It was only when eventually I could embrace that 'other' part that my wholeness, despite the acknowledgment of limitation, manifested to me. This embrace was a transitional step on the way to my identification of a new aspect of that eternal quality, love. Where there is love fear simply cannot exist and so, through love drawn from the depth of stillness, I truly took control of my life.

In being so self-defensive, I had been rather hard on myself and later discovered that I had also been pretty hard on others. Serenity and a clearer mind then assisted me to begin to let go of old judgments. In doing so I began, tripping and stumbling even still today, the lifelong lesson of forgiveness, where the practice of love through greater tolerance, patience and compassion can lead to happiness and peace.

As I began to understand the source of my *real* fear (a fear *for* myself and therefore a fear within myself), I realised that in coming to this point I had travelled full circle — from the unsettling times in childhood where tension became my weapon, to the moment when that weapon failed me by leading me into panic. Yet still I had trusted it — after all, tension was as natural to me then as breathing. I had faithfully employed tension as my greatest defence. Yet now I saw that tension in my body and in my mind had been my greatest obstacle of all.

But if tension was contagious, so also must be tranquillity. And so, as stillness gently moved me in a better direction, I came to learn that defending oneself, or fighting in this way, is hazardous. Ideally, acceptance and *management* of difficulties was the solution. If I had had the lifeskill of stillness years before, panic could never have occurred. If in those early weeks following that first panic attack I had been sent to Dr Meares for meditative stillness, I know I would never have endured those years with agoraphobia. I came to realise that agoraphobia is complicated by one's initial lack of understanding of the problem and the effect of various treatments which tend to prolong the state of fear. With fear intruding and with tension clouding any hope of objectivity, nothing is clear. Now

I was able to stand back and see that agoraphobia is far more simple than people have been led to believe. It is the lack of understanding and the resulting lack of corrective action that allows agoraphobia to develop into an ongoing 'disorder', an insurmountable problem that seems to defy solution and cause a state of awe for patient and therapist alike.

In searching for ways to improve our health and well-being, magazines and newspapers present many ideas, though frequently with a focus upon 'illness' rather than 'wellness'. In improving my own anxiety and therefore my general health, I came to understand the importance of holistic health care, *especially* the need to care for our mind. We readily rest our body when we are physically tired, but our mind, which does most of the work, rarely gets a break. It is clear that just as eating provides energy for our body from the intake of food, sleeping revives us through rest and exercise increases our physical fitness, meditative practices can provide ease for our mind and spirit. And so, these days, the word 'relax' is heard more often. However, this can become merely a catch word. At last I knew that real relaxation does not mean basking in the sunshine, playing sport or watching television. These are diversions and recreational activities which are also necessary. But experience had taught me that these alone will not bring calm to the troubled mind or reduce the level of tension and anxiety in the same way that meditative stillness will.

I find today that many people, like I once did, will say, when relaxation of any kind is suggested to them: 'I can't relax.' This tends to convince them of failure before they even try. A person may try once, and because he or she doesn't experience something new or discover an immediate solution to a problem, will give up, saying: 'It doesn't work.' But it *does* work! I have learned that every moment given to stillness is worthwhile. Like the squirrel that stores its food for the winter, we must be patient and store all those moments until one day the reward becomes obvious and we wonder how we ever lived without it.

People have asked me: 'What is so different about this way of meditation? We have tried this and that approach to meditation or relaxation and have not been helped significantly.' With most other methods of relaxation and meditation, some amount of mental effort is required, for example, awareness, recitation, breathing or visualising techniques.

What I learned from Ainslie Meares I now identify as *Stillness Meditation Therapy* (SMT^{TM}) – an approach that involves only the simple yet profound experience of one's own natural inner calm.

It is from that simplicity that powerful change occurs, the healing, the ease and the growing, without our *trying* at all. But while we are concentrating, enduring, thinking or focusing, even though in a relaxed manner, we will never experience *stillness* in the same way

When the experience of stillness is repeated, little by little the 'over-alertness' described earlier relaxes, and a calm attitude of functioning flows on and into the rest of life. This effect, then, is cumulative, giving rise to a generalised tranquillity as opposed to generalised agitation — a complete reversal of the way by which anxiety and tension increase. In other words, through stillness, one's internal response to living shifts and changes for the better and from this one begins to understand life a little differently, as happened in my own case.

In encouraging others to find this ease within stillness, I recognise that people who are anxious may hesitate to attempt something which at first may seem new and even slightly mysterious. It may well be new but there is nothing mysterious about being still; it is a completely natural response. But until this response becomes familiar to us, stillness may seem to be a practice that is a little different from what we are used to. The fact that the practice of *stillness* is different makes it something fascinating to explore. Anyway, it was Einstein himself who wrote:

> The fairest thing we can experience is the mysterious. It is the fundamental emotion which stands at the cradle of true art and true science. He who knows it not and can no longer wonder, no longer feel amazement, is as good as dead, a snuffed-out candle.

And so we begin to unravel the incomprehensible, and grasp a fragment of clarity within the mystery of life itself.

People may reject the concept of meditation, in the belief that it only brings temporary relief. This may be true of some techniques, which only bring about physical relaxation or which cannot bring about mental rest. Physical relaxation is only an *introduction* to a far deeper experience; for physical tension is only the visible weapon. Laying down of firearms is not sufficient to end a war! The correct practice of *stillness* goes to the heart of the matter. While one searches in vain for the elusive panacea to bring peace, the simple and obvious have been missed: our personal ability to access the natural serenity within. And without fail, should we falter, the repeated experience of stillness will renew our sense of well-being every time.

People need to feel in control, because all people crave security. Whether we realise it or not, to some extent we all aim to keep ourselves safe, to maintain control over our self and our life, to 'save our own skin'. This is perfectly reasonable. And this craving involves much more than remaining safe from physical harm. Here is where hidden fears, from the smallest to the most powerful — and our means of defending ourself against these — come into being. Here also is where I personally had made another mistake. For eight years I had sought freedom from fear and a sense of security from a limited therapeutic position. To develop that sense of security, and therefore our self-composure, much more is required; we need to attend to the needs of body, mind *and* spirit.

The practice of stillness provided security for my physical body and within my mind and it led in time to that 'something' that had been noticeably missing: spiritual sanctuary. There are many ways to honour our spirit, some of which I had already commenced through art and music, the natural world and more. But I believe this chapter would be incomplete without my exploration of the element of faith as it applied to me and my anxiety.

The word 'faith' implies a belief in something while having no clear proof of its existence. The word faith, though it can be widely applied, is usually linked to a concept of the Divine. As already noted, some people whose faith in God is strong may place their problems therein, obtaining help, solace and meaning by doing so. Others may find comfort from a faith that has emerged from specific religious teaching or from developed ideologies such as a Creative Source, Higher Power, Universal Energy. And others will find an equivalent faith and spiritual comfort by alternative means.

During my years of agoraphobia, my ability to access a satisfactory faith-consolation was erratic. Now something had changed and my understanding of faith began, with freshness, to stabilise and expand. I would not like to suggest that my own perception of faith must apply in the same way to others. But I do believe that it is important to address the needs of the spirit *in whichever way is appropriate to ourself.* In this part of the mystery of life, I feel it is necessary to be open-minded and listen to any possibility from which personal faith may grow or spiritual succour be obtained.

It seemed that in learning to 'let go' in stillness, and having begun to learn again the gift of trust, eventually I began to learn a new meaning of the word faith. Because of the practice of stillness in my life, in the first instance this lesson involved my trust and acceptance of simplicity and naturalness, where originally I was suspicious and leaned towards the need for substantiation through complex explanation or tactile matter.

Through this phase of personal growth, I learned how limited had been my former faith. I had always been a God-person, a believer, brought up in Catholicism. Following the teachings of my religion, in childhood I was devout, trusting implicitly. In adolescence, life was too much fun and, though attentive to religious practice, I was somewhat distracted. As a young adult, though I still practised my religion, I practically forgot God, paying lip-service only to what I then considered to be my faith. Later, in fear I prayed, my pleadings scattered without substance like idle leaves in an autumn wind, hoping He would hear me and miraculously change everything for the better. Then much later, through stillness and therefore less desperate, in my thirst for meaning I was drawn to explore spirituality, life and death by way of valuable, diverse and comparative theories, religions and philosophies. These explorations opened my eyes a little more and I came to see that during my years of fear, real faith in a Divine Power had been effectively absent to me. Though I wanted a personal God to fix the problem for me, I had, out of balance, put all my faith in something negative: the defensive use of tension.

As I more fully recognised the part I had played in my own suffering, I learned, with truer faith, that it was I (not God!) who was responsible for my situation. And the Christian message, the story which had been so much a part of my background, flew open with meaning.

Suffering had been what I had feared as I smothered a part of myself, my soul. And, like any polarity, suffering is part of a whole, its opposite I believe being love. Love is all-tolerant, forgiving, joyful and accepting — regardless. So suffering (which can always be linked to fear), when acknowledged, accepted and lived through, becomes love. As my life involuntarily changed through my faith in *stillness*, and I came to accept and appreciate myself regardless, I also came to discover a renewed faith in my God and the greater satisfaction of my deeper spiritual longings. Faith of this kind, I think, brings a particular kind of security — where the Divine meets our innermost human needs, towering above the kind of faith that exists only in the presence of other people or material comforts. I began to see God, the Almighty, the Creator, the Giver and the Lover, anew. And so I began to see myself, my life and my role in life as part of that creation and gradually all of me, my pain and the peace that had now entered my life, began to feel far more integrated. New faith in my God grew stronger as new faith in myself grew stronger.

There is a link here, I think, to the practice of stillness itself. To experience a sense of integration I had had to accept the wholeness of myself, my lightness and darkness, strength and weakness, ease and difficulty. Within our humanity we have been given the means — body, mind and spirit — to overcome difficulties as they occur. In mastering these, the energy within us, particularly that of our mind, is challenged. This is our most creative force at work (or perhaps play!) moving us to desire something different, stirring our need to educate ourself to change, inspiring our determination to succeed and tasking us to take the necessary steps to do so. And within our mind we can also learn to accept that beside the power of all that energy we also have the power to be still.

Meditation is one of the oldest and finest forms of prayer, yet in the main, the idea of meditation has been reserved for the cloisters, or we think it is only for Eastern mystics. Those who pray may do well to consider including times where the simple stillness of *being* occurs within the framework of their meditations or formal prayer. It is good to combine all of these; and if we want our stillness to be a prayer, it is a prayer. Like Elijah of old, we can find God 'not in the earthquake or the wind or the lightning, but in a gentle whisper'.

Those who do not pray can be led towards stillness through other avenues. At times I wondered myself why I hadn't discovered stillness and my newfound peace in other places: in the quiet of a cathedral, or my garden, or on a secluded beach surrounded by the rhythm of life, or the wonder of rainforest or bushland where nature and our instinct for nurturing is very close. Of course it *is* there, in all those places, just as it was in the garden of my childhood. But we have to need it. We have to seek it. And we have to have guidance. Then we will know how to find that stillness and the inner peace that comes from it, freely available to us forever, in any situation.

In reflecting upon my story, I had to some extent re-travelled the journey. The road during those eight years had been rocky at times, but I had finally found freedom from domination by fear and thus my story of fear drew to a close. Looking back, at the time I very much resented my struggle with agoraphobia. Now I was able to appreciate it as a detour that happened for the best. The experience, for all its discomfort and for what appeared to be a waste of precious years, made me a stronger and wiser woman.

It's important to acknowledge that by overcoming fear, I was not provided with lifelong immunity from stress, anxiety and tension. No-one can be so and remain alive! Living the journey taught me to value a balance of those elements as necessary motivators for all people, helping us strive towards fulfilment. However, I learned with great conviction that there is an easier way to do this.

Through *stillness meditation* I conquered fear. That was a triumph in itself, but it led to more. I had also gained a new way of living that brought personal transformation and enabled me to enjoy the fullness of living far more deeply than I had ever thought possible. And the greatest and smoothest diamond of all, my self-containment.

Life itself is not necessarily difficult — it is what we make of it that matters.

Chapter 17

WHEN ALL IS SAID AND DONE

❦

Not everything that counts can be counted.
Not everything that can be counted counts.

Albert Einstein

My original reason for writing this book was to put matters of anxiety to rest forever and get on with other things in life. I have been able to fulfill the latter part of that ambition, but the understanding, relief and management of anxiety is of such immense interest to me that helping others achieve these aims has formed a place in my destiny. And so, having gained personal insight through self-searching, clinical knowledge through professional training and a greater understanding of human emotion in working with my own clients, I became a 'wounded healer'. In witnessing at first hand the similarity between my own anxiety journey and the anxiety journeys of others, I have observed that all are basically of the same pattern:

- anxiety is an expression of fear and, in varying levels, is experienced by all people
- high levels of anxiety produce various unpleasant symptoms
- tension is adopted as a defence against those symptoms
- tension and anxiety feed on each other and produce increased anxiety
- stressful events further increase anxiety and tension
- anxiety levels then escalate to the point of panic
- to avoid further panic and to manage on-going symptoms, phobic defences and avoidance habits develop
- agoraphobia, the most severe anxiety reaction, is the result of the defence of persistent avoidance
- avoidance of any kind maintains the entire anxiety reaction.

Can you see the circular progression of personal defence, beginning small and growing out of control? Like a never-ending story, this pattern, formed from a natural inclination to protect oneself, becomes a negative defence strategy which can keep people trapped and disabled indefinitely!

Let's take a positive view. If the problem has developed as a natural progression of defence, then it follows that the healing will be natural also — providing one knows what to do and does what has to be done to allow the healing to happen.

Here then are my four essentials to achieve that:

- profound mental rest
- support from another source
- facing fear in tranquil action
- the pursuit of self-awareness.

Those steps can be summarised in four basic words touched upon earlier: *rest, reassurance, reassessment and renewal.*

Rest

As with any desired healing, rest is of the utmost importance and yet, the highly anxious person finds any kind of rest quite difficult because the mind cannot relax. So, in the matter of anxiety, mental rest is crucial for satisfactory healing. In my experience this rest can best be found in *stillness meditation* as already described.

I can't emphasise enough the high importance of effective mental rest – where the brain itself can regain (in Meares' terms), mental equilibrium. Anxiety holds such power over people – emotionally, mentally and physically – that it can be quite difficult to accept the possibility that long-term relief can be discovered quite simply and naturally. *Stillness meditation*, which is free of interference from further mental stimulus, is the key – and it's very practical, too, providing a positive way to begin to take control of the situation.

Perhaps such practical simplicity was what my local GP intended to convey all those years ago. There may also have been a grain of wisdom in my mother's desire to disregard my fear. Both could have done me a great service – but both lacked the ability to sufficiently express any underlying wisdom as I struggled too much to find a logical explanation and a 'quick modern fix' for my distress — when all I really needed was appropriate rest.

Reassurance

A great deal of reassurance is needed from a trusted companion or therapist. First attempts at *stillness meditation* may require the immediate presence of such a person as it is possible for the highly anxious person to temporarily experience intense physical or emotional discomfort while beginning the relaxing process. Since the heart of the matter is all about *letting go*, the trusted companion may need to verbalise time and again the reassurance that *letting go* is the way to break old defence habits and that *letting go* will eventually lead to calm, less reactive, living. And he or she also must reassure that this path to healing will take courage, time, practice, patience and perseverance.

Then, for the sufferer to *face* fear, he or she needs reassurance from trusted people (or from his or her own good judgment) that what is feared is not an external object — that what is feared are the *symptoms* of fear — and that it is by maintaining a high tension level that those symptoms remain active. The anxious person also needs reassurance that when the habit of fighting with tension is reversed and when calmness becomes the usual reaction, the anxiety and tension levels will decrease, allowing the symptoms to lessen and eventually disappear. And then, in time, there will no longer be any need to resort to phobic defences or to practise avoidance as confidence gradually returns.

Reassessment

Having introduced the practice of profound mental rest and garnered some new self-confidence, the situation can then be reassessed, so that one's own strategies for change can be applied. Added to that, it must be acknowledged within this reassessment that one must remain vigilant in maintaining calmness *forever*. In making progress to freedom, it is important that every situation is approached with *ease* and, as with any activity, the more you do, the more you *can* do. In the relief and management of anxiety, that response means truly facing your fear.

Renewal
At this point, life can be continued as normal. Then, if people so choose, they are literally free to explore their circumstances more deeply. This exploration will most likely lead to a renewal of their entire life through seeking self-awareness and the opportunity to make further changes or take new therapeutic paths toward greater personal development.

〜

Now I'd like to look at some further thoughts of my own to help you grasp these human reactions more fully. You may or may not agree with me, but I hope you will give them your consideration!

Anxiety as philosophy

Firstly, in helping others regain their confidence, I view anxiety quite positively, as part of a philosophical search for peace and 'wholeness', rather than a 'disorder' of a pathological or psychological nature. *Pathology* generally refers to that area of medicine that is concerned with the nature and treatment of disease. *Psychology* is the scientific study of human (and animal) behaviour. *Philosophy* leans towards an understanding of human beliefs and concepts. It is my belief that anxiety disorders and especially agoraphobia have become over-complicated through an inclination by professionals to ignore philosophical possibilities and either: (1) pathologise the condition, that is, treat these as one would treat an illness, by means of medication; or (2) psychologise the problem, that is, treat the condition through psychotherapy or psychoanalysis by attempting to uncover the origin of his or her anxiety or by means of behavioural modification modalities.

'Pathologising' the condition

Whilst generally favouring natural treatments I have always acknowledged that in some circumstances, medication is very necessary and help-ful – providing a period of respite – but only in the short term or taken occasionally as needed. As I've said prevously, all people benefit from or have need of some kind of crutch at certain times. I see medication as one of those crutches. I don't see 'drug therapy' for anxiety as a long term 'cure' or a real solution as this approach does nothing to negate the real problem, but only temporarily treats its symptoms. This means that treatment has very little lasting effect because anxiety will always rise above medication. The result is that more and more tablets are taken to fend off the recurring symptoms. So the effectiveness of the medication is diminished, leading to either increased or stronger dosages or experi-mentation with different types of medication.

It seems that anxiety sufferers are almost always automatically pre-scribed medication and for many, several varieties may have been taken consistently over many years. Even today, despite much controversial press relating to addiction, medical science relies heavily upon anti-depressants or tranquillisers. But certain people simply cannot tolerate these chemicals and for some, the medication itself can cause the very symptoms the patient is trying to be freed from. It's also very disturbing to see a readiness to use medication quite liberally with the very young.

It was 20 years or so ago that medical researchers initiated findings that pointed to biological and neurophysiological factors as the cause of anxiety and suggested that these conditions were fixed genetic imbalances with the only 'cure' being chemical remedies. As one who can claim to have experienced the extreme low of the agoraphobic reaction and a complete reversal of this, and as one who has witnessed so many others do the same, I've never been impressed by 'biological psychiatry' or by the pharmacological treatments surrounding these findings. It was Dr Ainslie Meares' view way back then that life itself is progressive and that as individuals we have the ability to change and progress in various ways. All living things are subject to variations in chemical and hormonal levels and we certainly inherit what we are from generations before us. But 'given the right conditions', i.e. his concept of mental rest, the mind has the capacity to self-manage anxiety relief through changes in brain func-tion. As referred to elsewhere, we now have the scientific term 'neuroplasticity' to demonstrate that the brain is pliable, able to correct imbalances and so-called genetic inheritances – and that this can be achieved through satisfactory meditation! So, earlier scientific assumptions would appear to have been incorrect. As I write this I wonder what is happening today with those people who have faultlessly adhered to those particular recommendations and prescriptions.

It would be disappointing, too, to see patients become medication dependent, reliant on chemicals which may ultimately provide only a placebo effect. Worse still, in that process, people can be be robbed of natural responses and sensitivity while remaining in a state of static fear, bereft of emotional or spiritual enrichment.

If it were so simple that all problems could be solved by taking 'pills', then humanity would indeed have discovered the secret of perfection. In our imperfect world, however, science can give us one solution which in turn very often creates the need for another. This can be readily seen in people such as those who state, 'He says I'll be on tablets for the rest of my life'; 'There's no cure for this, they say it's in your genes'; 'Nothing can be done for agoraphobia – the doctor says I'll have it for ever'. These attitudes seem to reflect limited thinking to say the least, and ultimately destroy even the slightest glimmer of hope.

'Psychologising' the Problem

The science of psychology and related therapies is very valuable. However, in the treatment of anxiety conditions where its purpose is to examine and act upon causal or behavioural factors, a psychological approach alone is of little immediate use, especially for the agoraphobic. For effectiveness, psychology relies upon open discussion and the gift of personal insight. The highly anxious person or typical agoraphobic shields him/herself from this kind of openness in their perennial passion for pretending that everything is all right, demonstrating this by being pleasant, co-operative and obliging, regardless of how they are really feeling. To maintain this façade, tension remains extremely high. And because tension blocks insight, there is very often little chance of the anxious person finding freedom along this therapeutic avenue *unless the tension —*

especially within the mind — is effectively lowered. So, while psychological approaches can be extremely helpful in dealing with life situations for many people, in the treatment of high anxiety I am aware of shortcomings.

Psychotherapy

It seems that anxiety, and the 'disorders' it produces, is in fact serving an important purpose, signalling an opportunity for people to move beyond the emotional barriers that constrain their lives. Therefore, anxiety ought to be regarded as a way to positive growth, whereas generally speaking anxiety is regarded negatively by most (professionals and patients alike) as something to be avoided at all costs. When tension is effectively reduced, and the road of life has opened again, anxiety can be seen as an expression of physical, emotional and spiritual need *involving* philosophical issues to be realised as truths. And this is where psychotherapy *can* be very helpful. Those who suffer anxiety, panic and agoraphobia are almost always of a sensitive temperament, possessing a precious inner life. And yet it is apparent that many anxious people have barely recognised, let alone truly accepted or investigated, their more ethereal side, which holds their deeper needs and longings. They, perhaps more than others, have a call to explore this. However, the mind must first be relaxed for this inward journey to begin.

Psychoanalysis

Similarly, some professionals favour psychoanalysis, as I have recorded within my story. In the psychoanalytic approach to treatment, childhood interactions and the role of the unconscious mind are explored. As can be seen within my reflections, it is relevant to problems to understand our beginnings and to recognise their influence, if any, upon where we are today. If the search for a solution does not progress beyond the past, the person may remain frozen there and a great deal of unproductive resentment and anger may simmer. This approach can also lead to therapeutic dependency, frustration, too much introspection and the possibility of fostering blame. Rather than dealing positively with these feelings, the person may hold others responsible for his or her present predicament — and this is unjust. The first rule of self-care is responsibility for the self. One may not be responsible for all that has already happened, but one is, and must continue to be, responsible for all that is now and is still to come.

Both psychotherapy and psychoanalysis also require the use of logic in order to succeed. While for example, the anxiety level of agoraphobia may not be an organic disease neither does it exist at a logical, intellectual level within the person's mind. Rather, this is an emotional defence against the unpleasant feelings associated with an attack of panic. Such a powerful inner defence cannot be overcome by logical intervention. And while psychotherapeutic and psychoanalytic approaches can be extremely helpful in gaining knowledge of the real cause of the anxiety, alone they are unlikely to alleviate anxiety *symptoms*. For, even when the origin of the anxiety is consciously known – and this may take a very long time to be revealed – unless the mind has somehow regained serenity and the excess tension has lowered, the symptoms and phobic reactions will continue.

Behavioural approaches

In looking at the prospect of changing one's behaviour, the same rational requirement continues. My friend could not help me to overcome my fear in a logical or rational way in his attempt at behavioural therapy. It is well nigh impossible to address logically or rationally the defences that dwell powerfully and instinctively in our emotional being. Furthermore, rational thinking and the use of logic drives us to continue to fight. And the more we fight, emotionally or rationally, the more we have to fear! So the behavioural approach to treatment I have found to be merely palliative, bringing only the possibility of temporary relief.

People may, with a great deal of effort and will-power, learn to force themselves beyond fear. But is it right to push people to their limits, to encourage force, albeit kindly, through a fearful situation, while most likely creating immense strain in the process? In these circumstances, it is certain that in time this effort will all be too much, as a great deal more tension – both physical and mental – will have been required to meet the goal. This, of course, is counter-productive and once more the anxious person will be left despondent, frustrated and disappointed in what will appear to be a permanently unsolvable problem. Moreover, from forced action, nothing will have been learned to enrich the spirit or beg the opportunity to grow.

Cognitive Behavioural Therapy

Most popular for anxiety disorders among many therapists today is Cognitive Behavioural Therapy (CBT). This approach, a derivative of Rational Emotive Therapy, comprises breathing and relaxation techniques, the perceptual understanding of the anxiety-producing situation and the aim of changing negative thoughts surrounding that situation through positive re-conditioning. Again, the very word 'cognitive' means the use of the logical or rational mind. But at least this form of treatment acknowledges the need for relaxation and in that, it certainly has attributes. However, I have reservations about its supposed success rate. Many people travel that path and find some relief, yet still experience panic attacks and are still affected by their phobia, accepting these as part of a 'disorder' they have now learned to live with. Any treatment of a rational or behavioural kind may see people respond and notice improvement for a time. But in my experience, the mind requires a great deal more rest than most relaxation methods can offer – and until such rest can effectively reduce anxiety levels, fear will inevitably return. A serene mind cannot be obtained while mental activity or stimulus is advocated. Nor will the internal response (or attitude to life) alter sufficiently from living defensively with tension to living calmly with ease while ever treatment relies upon any form of cognition. Somehow, the mind must first be satisfactorily calmed!

A philosophical view

I have said the most extreme reaction to high anxiety is that of agoraphobia. In earlier editions of this book and again in an earlier chapter here I have described agoraphobia as 'the fear of leaving the safety of home or 'the fear of fear' and these definitions remain adequate. However, I would now go further to say:

Agoraphobia is the fear of losing control for fear of taking control.

Here again is a case of opposites: anxiety and its symptoms push us to the edge of losing control and the defences we have created drive us to hold on in a misguided bid to keep control. But the more we hold on, the more anxiety (or fear) will push! On that life-defining occasion of my first panic attack, the dominant threat I felt was that of being removed from the scene with no control over the situation, being unable to properly communicate and somehow *losing the integrity of myself, my identity* — shades of my early life! This is the common reaction of acute anxiety. Any threat to one's self is the ultimate human danger and amounts, philosophically, to loss of control.

The intensely anxious person desperately fears losing control, and at an inner level this is a fear he or she has created while attempting to maintain a preferred image, striving to feel fully accepted in the world. The onset of panic threatens to expose all — in the dread of a crumbling façade and the risk of likely judgment, criticism or public shame. But the highly anxious person also desperately fears *taking control* — for to do so would involve letting go of the defences he or she fights with to prevent loss of control. Taking *true* control does not involve fighting. It involves *letting go* — of tension *and* of the belief that there is something we must defend ourselves from. In agoraphobia for example, letting go of one's defences is what is feared and avoided — not merely out of fear of an attack of panic, but out of fear of our whole undoing. So there is a double-edge to high anxiety: *the fear of losing control, for fear of taking control.* Paradoxically, it's in the letting go that we successfully move through both edges of fear, with the result that we can then take calm control of our life.

All things in life have a practical value, anxiety conditions and phobias no less. The purpose or usefulness of a phobia as a defence lies, I believe, within the definition above. From a philosophical perspective, to understand *why* we are not taking true control we must look closely at panic, the emotional experience that the potential agoraphobic spends his or her life trying to avoid.

Of panic
Panic is defined as *the sudden overwhelming onset of intense apprehension,*

fear or terror, often associated with a feeling of impending doom — in other words, the feeling of loss of control. If we think about panic as it is commonly recognised, we can see that people feel panic-stricken when faced with a chaotic situation or one over which they have no personal control. For example, people may experience mass panic in a crowded place if told the building is on fire. The fire is beyond the control of each person present, yet each fears for his or her own safety. A sense of urgency and helplessness then occurs and as nothing *can* be done, the fight or flight reaction escalates and becomes *panic* where people irrationally fight or attempt to flee from the threatening location. Their lives arc virtually in someone else's hands; the theatre manager, the ushers, the security guard, the fire brigade, medical help and so on. None of these are within a person's individual control.

Yet each person instinctively must attempt to take control. As discussed earlier, a level of control is necessary or life would be constantly chaotic. But in situations of great threat or public danger, usually there is no way one *can* take control and panic is the only emotional release or action available. Under these circumstances, people may experience the same or similar feelings as those experienced by the victim of the apparently spontaneous panic attack associated with intense anxiety. For those whose anxiety has reached agoraphobic proportions, though, there is no fire or any other visible threat to escape from. For some reason, unclear at the time, he or she is also trying *to take control* of a particular situation. In a bid to fight, or to defend themselves, tension has increased. As nothing in life happens without purpose, there *must* be a purpose in these panicky feelings — even though it seems that nothing dangerous is imminent.

Of agoraphobia
For the agoraphobic person, the purpose of panic is this: danger is lurking wherever he or she is has reached *an emotionally vulnerable situation*. By this I mean a situation that threatens to expose one's major vulnerability and therefore the integrity of the self. This is a fundamentally philosophical issue. Through the need to save face by pretending all is well, by stoically fighting to keep false control and by striving to prove oneself beyond imagined shame, doubt, unworthiness or failure, the ten-

sion level has risen too high (in much the same way as I have described in my own case). Panic is the response when one experiences a feeling that there is no escape, there is nowhere left to go — except to a place (or person) that represents unconditional safety, usually home!

Those who become anxious and succumb to agoraphobia, I find, are expressing by means of panic what they cannot yet recognise in themselves. Nor can they express in any other way what is taking place within. How understandable, then, that people who experience panic begin to fight more and more, literally for their lives.

Let me take you, the agoraphobic reader, back for a moment to your first panic attack. You had been living with tension for some time, brought about most likely, by beliefs you hold about yourself. Recent stress had been high. You were notably exhausted. You were under pressure and you had responsibilities to cope with. In dealing with everything, you had become even more generally tense. You were out of the house, probably unaccompanied, and you felt ill and disoriented. Those feelings caused fear and anxiety to push your panic button; as panic rose within you, a sense of impending disaster overwhelmed. You felt you were about to lose control of your reason — or that perhaps you might be facing sudden death, or at least uncontrollable collapse of some kind.

What you dreaded in that instant was the exposure of your human vulnerability, a fragile part of yourself amounting to immense insecurity — and therefore the risk of your own public undoing. This is why at those times symptoms such as *feeling lost, diminished, out of balance, de-personalised and fragmented* occur. (Interestingly, when feeling safe, people are usually feeling *whole* and *in control,* and at those times they are symptom-free.) Unconsciously, the agoraphobia sufferer has reached a point where, out of self-defence, this person has no more control over certain aspects of life than the members of the theatre audience have over a fire — *so panic occurs as the instinctive defence of tension increases.* It is easy, then, to begin to restrict oneself more and more in avoidance of panic, thus setting up the agoraphobic syndrome.

Prior to this occurrence, within your learned attitude to life you had found personal security through increased tension and 'toughing it out'. Unknown to you, this defence had been a contributing factor to your panic attack. Now, to avoid panic occurring again and in an attempt to retain dignity and integrity, in further self-defence, you have allowed your tension levels to increase so greatly that you remain in a state of constant anxiety, ever-steeling yourself to fend off more rising symptoms.

Of personal change

The description of my early married life at the beginning of this book fits very accurately the experiences of many who come to me today as clients. Typically this person is female, often aged between twenty and forty, perhaps married and often the mother of young children. She will have a high sense of responsibility to others. She will be strong, though sensitive, creative and talented, often exhibiting the frustration of giftedness thwarted by lack of self-fulfilment. She will not be able to recognise her true feelings, being instead very aware of her *reactions* to her feelings in the form of anxiety and helplessness. Quite likely she will be physically and mentally exhausted. And she will have experienced significant stress, leading to anxiety, panic and perhaps agoraphobia. At some earlier time, she began her fight with tension, practising self-defence rather than self-reliance. In this she preserves a certain image for the world, and in her self-doubt, negates the wholeness (or integrity) of herself to the extent that she depends upon objects, or others, to provide her with a sense of her own existence. Her greatest dilemma lies in her inability to accept herself as wholly as she accepts others. As yet she doesn't recognise that whatever she is fighting against within herself is generally a belief of her own making based upon her own judgment. It should be noted that what we accept and believe as truths sometimes need questioning.

So while much has been achieved with regard to women's rights in society, it can be seen that many women do not understand the true meaning of the word 'liberation'. And what of liberation for the men who fall into the category of anxiety sufferers? While total human freedom amounts to an impossibility, to aim for true liberation is to have the ability to accept the truth of what we are with the desire and the means to change or improve what we are not, *free from the defences that create limited living.*

Sometimes the anxious state is associated with low self-esteem. This may be so for some, but most anxious people I meet seem to follow a similar pattern to my own. I had reasonable self-esteem. That was what I was fighting to keep. But I was also fighting to control my vulnerable side — so that the false beliefs upon which I judged myself so harshly would not escape and let me down completely. When I should have been working positively to fulfil my life — and even more importantly, correct the real inadequacies within myself — I was instead wasting energy, fighting negatively against something within myself that didn't truly exist.

When agoraphobic, I remained stuck in a self-imposed restriction where I avoided the symptoms of fear while maintaining tension, in the hope that by this means I could control my life. My example of trying to dispel fear by having a new hair-cut was a small attempt to take control; my experiment backfired because, at the time, I had no understanding of why I took that action. Therefore, once home again I immediately reverted to my ingrained style of living, the old learned habit — fighting my cause with tension. In other words, I was fighting a personal battle for self-preservation. Once again, control over one's life cannot be gained by fighting. As soon as I ceased my fight, I had won the battle. From *stillness meditation*, true control came later, with the dissolving of tension and the disappearance of fear. Then self-acceptance was awakened, the acceptance of my wholeness — the good and the less good within me — offering the possibility of fruitful change.

And *that* is when one can successfully turn to the science of psychology and enjoy the benefits of increased self-knowledge, awareness and new life direction either through psychotherapy, psychoanalysis or behavioural change. Or perhaps a complementary route, that of spiritual direction in the philosophy of your preference, may be an option for many?

Commitment to self care

Caring for oneself is a life-long project — a kind of challenge to *live well*. Like a strong relationship, good health and a good life do not 'just happen' as many might hope; we must be prepared to work at achieving this state. So in the serious desire to over-come the obstacles of anxiety, panic and fear, it is necessary to be committed to this cause.

The film *City of Joy*, based on the book by Dominique Lapierre, uses the principle that in life we have three options:

- to run
- to 'spectate'
- to commit.

Most people have known at some time the experience of running away from life's challenges. In my years of agoraphobia, I did my share of running, only to receive in return for that effort ever-increasing fear and an all-pervading emptiness, to say nothing of a host of other accompanying negative emotions.

It is tempting too, for the fainthearted to 'spectate'. Why not, after all, let others do it all for us while we try to remain safe and comfortable? But this way of life, too, is profitless and only emphasises the dependency people have come to accept: the doctor knows best, the tablets will cure this condition … everything will be all right when . . .? Being a spectator in life also leads us down an empty path.

But commitment — to oneself and to the world we live in — is the threshold we long for, the threshold to the wellspring of the goodness of life. Commitment to any worthwhile cause will always bring positive results. It sparks our motivation and kindles hope when hope seems to be flagging. Commitment is the tool that gets things done. We must, therefore, make commitment a priority and, through it, take responsibility for ourselves.

With commitment we can then begin to eradicate excessive tension by practising with purpose, *stillness meditation* as I have outlined in this book. As its serenity enters our lives, from it will be distilled the answers we are seeking and the *lasting* solution to the problem of this kind of fear.

Make it happen!

A life free of problems is a life without experience and, perhaps, without meaning. The experience of agoraphobia in my life helped me towards richer personal development and a more profound understanding of life and of human kind. We are all 'amateur actors', feeling our way, learning by our mistakes and our successes; even the steps which sometimes seem to be backward eventually take us forward in the continuing growth towards completeness. And so we collect life's experiences as we might collect shells from the beach.

We should remember that, while sometimes those seashells are flung on to the sand in the midst of the storm, without fail, once the storm has passed, more shells will be gently laid there by the peaceful waters of a new day. As a child I found peace in Nessa's garden. Somewhere, in everyone's memory, is a 'garden' of some kind where trouble is washed away by tranquillity. I use the example of the garden, not as an end in itself, but only to awaken within the reader's spirit the tiniest possibility of stillness and the wish to seek further. For it is well to recapture that memory and realise its value. It could be just the sparkle of light necessary to help you on your way. It is necessary too, to grasp the fact that suffering, whatever it may be, is not necessarily something to be avoided or of which to be ashamed, but an opportunity for life enhancement. *Stillness meditation* is, in my experience, the skill by which that suffering can be more easily accepted, transformed and overcome. It is also a skill of sustenance for one's entire life, come what may, for there definitely will be other challenges to meet!

I recognise my good fortune in overcoming fear. Although eight years seemed a long time to me then, it is nothing at all compared to those who have known fear for twenty-eight or thirty-eight years. But this doesn't mean that my understanding of the problem of anxiety (or fear) is any the less, or that those who have suffered longer cannot change.

Here now, is a confession. During those years of fear I thought I would never forget one unpleasant moment. But in the original telling of this story and in now reviewing it years later, I have had to take my mind right back with some effort to recall the detail of that experience. A statement such as that, I think, holds sufficient conviction for the reader to know that anxiety, panic and fear definitely belong to my past.

It is my privilege to have shared all this with you. I trust that my story will continue to bring the outcomes of fear to greater recognition and provide some insight, hope and the possibility of relief for a great many people. To wish an easy road is to deny you adventure. I wish you, instead, a fulfilling journey upon which you will find a tranquil return to the truth and loving wholeness of yourself — and a future of contentment where all your dreams will be fulfilled.

I began this book by recalling a conversation with a stranger on a train. His thoughts seem a fitting expression to close with: 'People are scared, you know'! But it is generally because they are tense. People are tense, you know. But we don't have to be — there is a rewarding alternative!

APPENDIX: DR AINSLIE MEARES

Courtesy of Sylvia Black
(née Meares), April 1999

Ainslie Dixon Meares, BAgS, MD, BS, DPM, was an Australian psychiatrist, most famous as a pioneer in recognising stress as a major cause of illness and in teaching people how it could be overcome through meditation. He wrote of his work in thirty books, among them the international best seller *Relief Without Drugs* (Great Britain: Souvenir Press Ltd, 1968), and over one hundred medical papers.

Dr Meares was born in Melbourne, Australia, in 1910. He studied medicine at Melbourne University and graduated just as World War II broke out. He enlisted in the Australian Infantry Forces and became a regimental medical officer. Towards the end of the war he was stationed at an army hospital in Goulburn, New South Wales, where he treated soldiers who had become mentally disturbed by the trauma of their war experiences. This was probably the most significant point in Dr Meares' career because it was here that he made his decision to make psychiatry his life's work.

After the war he joined a practice at the Royal Melbourne Hospital, but quickly became disenchanted with the techniques of orthodox psychiatry such as psychoanalysis, electric shock treatment and drug therapy. Two years later he opened his own private practice.

He turned first to hypnosis. It was not the authoritative form of hypnosis where the hypnotist attempts to remove the patient's symptoms by suggestion that interested him, but hypno-analysis. This was considered to be a quicker version of psychoanalysis. In the hypnotic state the patient's inhibitions are reduced and the mind is therefore more open to revealing inner conflicts. However, Dr Meares soon discovered that sometimes patients would get better after hypnosis without their deepseated problems ever being discovered. In this state their mental function had reverted to a biologically primitive mode of uncritical functioning and a state of calm, which Dr Meares called *atavistic regression*.

By now Dr Meares had come to believe that organic illness and psychological illness were not mutually exclusive — that in fact they were different manifestations of the same thing. Further, he was sure that there was one common cause, and that was anxiety. He reasoned that stress increased the levels of natural cortisone in the body which then inhibited the body's auto-immune system and left it open to illness.

To learn more about hypnosis and its effects on the brain he travelled all over the world studying various hypnotic states and their role in the lives of people of different cultures. He observed macumba in Brazil, voodoo in Haiti and fire-walking in Bali; he visited witch doctors in Africa and lived for a while with Zen Buddhist monks in Japan. But it was one particular yogi he met and sat with in the foothills of the Himalayas who proved to be a pivotal factor in Dr Meares' life. This man was 134 years old, meditated for sixteen hours each day and his inner calm was palpable. When asked if he were ever troubled by pain, his answer was that he did feel pain but that there was no hurt in it. He was aware of the warning signals of the pain and could respond accordingly, but he was not discomforted by it.

As the two men sat together sometimes they would not talk, but in the yogi's presence Dr Meares would find himself drifting into a state of reverie and afterwards would feel himself changed by this — he had taken on some of the yogi's calm.

Back in Melbourne, Dr Meares was determined to learn to meditate and through it to master pain. He started by lying on a low stone garden wall, the idea being to overcome discomfort, not to go to sleep. He learnt to shut out all thought and to allow his mind simply to drift. He found that the sensation of calm and ease lasted well beyond the period of meditation.

The next step was to overcome pain. He practised by piercing his skin with pins and laying burning string across his forearm. But the real test was to have an abscessed molar removed without anaesthetic (1963). It proved to be a much more difficult extraction than expected, with the dentist having to chisel away some of the jaw bone to get the tooth out sideways. Yet, while Dr Meares was aware of what was happening, he felt no pain; there was minimal bleeding and no post-operative discomfort. Other similar experiments followed with the same results.

It was time now to introduce atavistic regression (mental relaxation) to his patients without hypnosis. Dr Meares put what he had learnt from the yogi into practice. Speech makes people alert, so any communication he used had to be non-verbal. He, himself, had to exude calm, like the yogi, to create an atmosphere in which the patient, too, would feel calm. If the patient showed any sign of anxiety Dr Meares would respond with a gentle touch to the arm or a low murmur.

In the years that followed, Dr Meares successfully treated hundreds of patients for anxiety and pain by showing them how to achieve mental relaxation — his approach to meditation.

By 1975 Dr Meares sought to probe even further into the powers of the mind. He now wanted to see if by intensive meditation he could influence the effects of cancer. His colleagues in the medical profession saw this as an impossible and futile pursuit. He could not look to them for support or referrals and so he needed to advertise for patients who would be prepared to take part in his experiment. But doctors are not allowed to advertise, so he took the decision to formally retire from medical practice and concentrate entirely on his work in meditation.

Inevitably, patients were slow to make themselves available at first and those who did come were those for whom all other avenues of treatment had failed. They were terminal patients and Dr Meares was a last resort. But as word of his work spread, gradually the numbers built up and after ten years he was able to say confidently that intensive meditation could influence the growth of cancer. Nearly all his patients suffered less discomfort and pain and needed fewer drugs. Nearly all achieved an inner calm and a sense of peace, no longer concerned about death. Many patients exhibited a remarkable slowing of the growth of their cancers and lived considerably longer than expected. Some patients achieved remission.

Dr Meares died in 1986.

ABOUT THE AUTHOR

A Melbourne meditation consultant and psychotherapist, Pauline Mc Kinnon has maintained the unique teachings of Dr Ainslie Meares for over twenty five years, offering relief and management of anxiety through Stillness Meditation Therapy (SMT™). She also conducts a practitioner training course in SMT and is a regular guest presenter for corporate bodies, community centres, support groups, schools, hospitals and universities.

In publishing *Quiet Magic* and *Help Yourself and Your Child to Happiness* in the 1990s, Pauline acted upon her concern for young people experiencing anxiety. These books have led to SMT programs being successfully introduced into some Australian primary schools.

Pauline balances her professional role with family life and also enjoys singing. She may be contacted at:

The Pauline McKinnon Life Development Centre
PO Box 151
Kew East 3102, Victoria, Australia
www.lifedevelopmentcentre.com.au

Purchase of further resources may be made online or by writing to the above address.

Listen to Pauline McKinnon

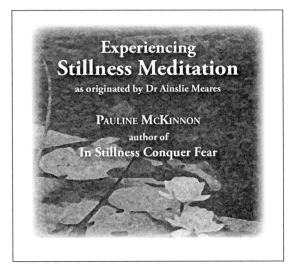

Experiencing
Stillness Meditation
as originated by Dr Ainslie Meares

PAULINE McKINNON
author of
In Stillness Conquer Fear

AUDIO PRESENTATION
CD ISBN 978 1920721 82 4 $19.95

If you are too distant to share meditation time with Pauline, or if you simply feel the need for help with your daily practise or a glimpse into her sessions, this introduction to *stillness* is for you. A natural and simple lifeskill for tranquillity, this style of meditation brings freedom from anxiety and tension and the discovery of harmony, health and happiness — the qualities of a better life. Instructional and experiential, this audio presentation will be of interest and guidance to those who seek stress free living.

Contents

1. Introduction
2. What is stillness meditation?
3. Major benefits of stillness
4. Further benefits
5. Towards tranquillity
6. Before commencing practice
7. Requirements for practice
8. Basic introduction to stillness for beginners
9. Introduction to a deeper experience of stillness
10. Introduction to a more complete experience of stillness

johngarrattpublishing
1300 650 878